LINEAR OPERATORS FOR QUANTUM MECHANICS

Linear Operators for Quantum Mechanics

THOMAS F. JORDAN

Department of Physics
University of Pittsburgh

John Wiley & Sons, Inc.

New York · London · Sydney · Toronto

Library of Congress Catalog Card Number: 68-8104
Cloth: SBN 471 45040 5 Paper: SBN 471 45041 3
Printed in the United States of America

PREFACE

This is intended to be a companion to quantum-mechanics books. It treats the mathematics of linear operators used in quantum mechanics. Other elements of quantum mechanics are included only when they are needed for motivation or completeness. Different students may study the mathematical aspects at different times, depending on their backgrounds, interests, and needs. This is one reason for a separate treatment of the mathematics. I hope that in this compact presentation it will be easy for students of quantum mechanics to see the logic and simplicity of its mathematical structure.

My motivation to write this book has come from teaching first-year graduate quantum mechanics at the Universities of Rochester and Pittsburgh. The presentation is intended for a reader at that level. To round it out I have included topics not usually studied in the first year but which most students of quantum mechanics want to know sooner or later.

Originally quantum mechanics was atomic physics, but now it is also a basic language for solid-state, nuclear, and particle physics. The grammar of this language is the mathematics of linear operators. My philosophy is simply that knowing the grammar makes it easier to understand the language and easier to use it.

I take an entirely conventional view of the mathematical foundations of quantum mechanics. Most of it is in von Neumann's book. For equations of motion and representations of symmetry transformations I follow Wigner and Bargmann. The picture is filled in with recent work; for example, that of Jauch and co-workers.

My only serious deviation from standard physics practice is in diagonalizing operators. It seems to me that the difference between continuous and point spectra is important. I use projection operators on the ordinary Hilbert space, which naturally emphasizes this difference, instead of using vectors of infinite length to treat the continuous spectrum in analogy to the point spectrum. This just requires thinking about integrals with respect to $dF(x)$ instead of $f(x)dx$.

The reader needs no technical knowledge of Lebesgue or Stieltjes integrals. An intuitive understanding of integration is sufficient.

I never give a proof just to establish that a statement is true. For that I have thought it sufficient to supply a reference. The proofs are intended to explain how or why statements are true and to provide exercises using some of the concepts or techniques. The references are not always intended to give credit for original work. They indicate where I think reading can continue with the most profit or least trouble.

Sections 20, 28, and 32 are not needed for the other sections that follow. It may be best to skip them the first time through. Section 11 also could be skipped.

THOMAS F. JORDAN

Pittsburgh, Pennsylvania
January 1968

ACKNOWLEDGMENTS

John R. Taylor responded very generously to my statement that I would appreciate criticism of the manuscript. He returned a thoroughly marked-up copy and spent many hours going over it with me to explain his ideas, in addition to writing letters about various points as he thought of them. This was immensely helpful to me as I worked through the manuscript again and led to significant improvements in every chapter. I am very grateful.

Leonard Parker made a detailed review of the manuscript at the request of the editor at John Wiley and Sons. His page-by-page and line-by-line criticism was an excellent guide for working through the manuscript. When I finished, I was so pleased to have had such a careful review that I asked to know the identity of the reviewer so that I could acknowledge his contribution to the book.

I want to thank Philip Stehle for much good advice about writing books in general and good criticism of this one in particular. I want to thank Johan de Swart, Gordon Fleming, Wolfgang Kundt, and Lochlainn O'Raifeartaigh for helpful comments, discussions, and criticism.

To Johan de Swart I am indebted also for a course of lectures that started my interest in the mathematics of linear operators some years ago.

Finally, I want to acknowledge my indebtedness to George Sudarshan who, first in teaching me to understand and appreciate the mathematical structure of quantum mechanics, and in discussing many of these topics, has contributed decisively to the concept and contents of this book and to my inspiration to write it.

T. F. J.

CONTENTS

LINEAR OPERATORS FOR QUANTUM MECHANICS

1

LINEAR SPACES
AND LINEAR
FUNCTIONALS

1. VECTORS

The mathematical structures of quantum mechanics are built on linear spaces. To get the concept of a linear space we need only to generalize from vectors in ordinary three-dimensional position space to vectors in a space of arbitrary dimension. At the same time we consider vectors whose components in each direction are complex instead of real numbers. The algebraic properties of vectors, that they can be added and multiplied by numbers, are abstracted in the following.

Definitions. A *linear space* or *vector space* is a set of elements, called *vectors*, with an operation of *addition*, which for each pair of vectors ψ and ϕ specifies a vector $\psi + \phi$, and an operation of *scalar multiplication*, which for each vector ψ and number a specifies a vector $a\psi$ such that

(i) $\psi + \phi = \phi + \psi$, (ii) $\psi + (\phi + \chi) = (\psi + \phi) + \chi$,

(iii) a unique zero vector 0 has the property that $\psi + 0 = \psi$,

(iv) $a(\psi + \phi) = a\psi + a\phi$, (v) $(a + b)\psi = a\psi + b\psi$,

(vi) $a(b\psi) = (ab)\psi$, (vii) $1 \cdot \psi = \psi$,

(viii) $0 \cdot \psi = 0$

for any vectors ψ, ϕ, and χ and numbers a and b. The numbers are called *scalars.* The vector space is called *complex* or *real*, depending on whether complex numbers or only real numbers are used as scalars.[1]

Property (viii) justifies using the same symbol 0 for both the zero vector and the number zero. We use the notation $-\psi$ for $(-1)\psi$ and $\phi - \psi$ for $\phi + (-1)\psi$.

As examples of linear spaces consider the following:

(i) The set of all n-tuples of numbers with addition of two vectors $\psi = (x_1, x_2, \ldots, x_n)$ and $\phi = (y_1, y_2, \ldots, y_n)$ defined by $\psi + \phi = (x_1 + y_1, x_2 + y_2, \ldots, x_n + y_n)$ and multiplication of the vector ψ by a scalar a defined by $a\psi = (ax_1, ax_2, \ldots, ax_n)$. We refer to this as n-dimensional Euclidean space.

(ii) The set of all infinite sequences of numbers $(x_1, x_2, \ldots, x_k \ldots)$ such that $\sum_{k=1}^{\infty} |x_k|^2$ is finite with addition and scalar multiplication defined componentwise as in the previous example.[2] This space is called l^2.

(iii) The set of all continuous functions of a real variable x with addition of two vectors ψ and ϕ defined by $(\psi + \phi)(x) = \psi(x) + \phi(x)$ and multiplication of a vector ψ by a scalar a defined by $(a\psi)(x) = a\psi(x)$.

(iv) The set of all functions ψ of a real variable x which are solutions of the differential equation $d^2\psi(x)/dx^2 = -\omega^2\psi(x)$ with addition and scalar multiplication defined pointwise as in the previous example.

(v) The set of all functions ψ of a real variable x for which the Lebesgue integral $\int |\psi(x)|^2 \, dx$ is finite with addition and scalar multiplication defined pointwise as in the preceding examples.[3] We refer to a space of this kind as L^2. It may be defined with a finite or infinite range of the variable x or with functions of more than one variable.

Each example can be either a complex or real vector space, depending on whether the numbers or functions used are complex or real. These examples also illustrate the concept of a *linear manifold* in a vector space. This is a subset of vectors which is a linear space itself. We find n-dimensional Euclidean spaces as linear manifolds in l^2 and spaces (iv) of solutions of oscillator equations as linear manifolds in the space (iii) of continuous

---

[1] We will continue to do things in a way which is applicable to either a real or complex vector space.

[2] That the sum of two vectors satisfies the condition for l^2 is shown by Minkowski's inequality $(\sum_{k=1}^{n} |x_k + y_k|^2)^{1/2} \leq (\sum_{k=1}^{n} |x_k|^2)^{1/2} + (\sum_{k=1}^{n} |y_k|^2)^{1/2}$ as $n \to \infty$. For each finite n this is just the triangle inequality for lengths of vectors in n-dimensional Euclidean space; see Section 2, *Inner Products.*

[3] For a proof that the sum of two square-integrable functions is square-integrable and for a general discussion of the Lebesgue integral and L^2 spaces, see F. Riesz and B. Sz.-Nagy, *Functional Analysis*, translated by L. F. Boron (F. Ungar Publishing Co., New York, 1955), pp. 5–6 and Chapter 2.

functions. It is often correct to call a linear manifold a *subspace*, but the words have precisely the same meaning only for finite-dimensional subspaces.[4]

Definitions.   A set of vectors $\psi_1, \psi_2, \ldots, \psi_n$ is *linearly dependent* if there are scalars $a_1, a_2, \ldots, a_n$, not all zero, such that $a_1\psi_1 + a_2\psi_2 + \cdots + a_n\psi_n = 0$; it is *linearly independent* if $\sum_{k=1}^{n} a_k\psi_k = 0$ is possible only for $a_1 = a_2 \cdots = a_n = 0$. An infinite set of vectors is *linearly independent* if every finite subset is linearly independent; otherwise it is *linearly dependent*. A linear space is *n-dimensional* if it contains n linearly independent vectors but not $n + 1$. If it contains n linearly independent vectors for every positive integer n, it is *infinite-dimensional*. A set of vectors $\psi_1, \psi_2, \ldots, \psi_k$ *spans* a linear space if each vector in the space is a linear combination $a_1\psi_1 + a_2\psi_2 + \cdots + a_k\psi_k$ of the vectors $\psi_1, \psi_2, \ldots, \psi_k$ with scalars $a_1, a_2, \ldots, a_k$. A set of vectors $\psi_1, \psi_2, \ldots, \psi_k$ is a *basis* for a linear space if it is a linearly independent set and spans the space.

For example, a set of vectors $\psi_1, \psi_2, \ldots, \psi_n$ spans the linear manifold of all linear combinations $a_1\psi_1 + a_2\psi_2 + \cdots + a_n\psi_n$; if the set of vectors $\psi_1, \psi_2, \ldots, \psi_n$ is linearly independent, it is a basis for this linear manifold. In particular each nonzero vector spans a one-dimensional subspace. The concepts just defined are tied together further by the following.

Theorem 1.1.   A linear space is *n*-dimensional if and only if it has a basis of n vectors.

Proof.   Suppose the space has a basis of n vectors $\phi_1, \phi_2, \ldots, \phi_n$. This is a linearly independent set. To show that the space is *n*-dimensional we show that no set of $n + 1$ vectors $\psi_1, \psi_2, \ldots, \psi_{n+1}$ is linearly independent. Since the vectors $\phi_1, \phi_2, \ldots, \phi_n$ span the space, each vector ψ_j for $j = 1, 2, \ldots, n + 1$ is a linear combination $\psi_j = \sum_{k=1}^{n} a_{kj}\phi_k$. If the vectors $\psi_1, \psi_2, \ldots, \psi_{n+1}$ were linearly independent, there would be no scalars $c_1, c_2, \ldots, c_{n+1}$ other than zeros which satisfy

$$\sum_{k=1}^{n} \sum_{j=1}^{n+1} a_{kj} c_j \phi_k = \sum_{j=1}^{n+1} c_j \psi_j = 0.$$

But this is satisfied if $\sum_{j=1}^{n+1} a_{kj} c_j = 0$ for $k = 1, 2, \ldots, n$, and these n linear equations certainly have a solution other than zeros for the $n + 1$ scalars c_j.

If the space is *n*-dimensional, there are n linearly independent vectors $\phi_1, \phi_2, \ldots, \phi_n$. For any vector ψ the set of $n + 1$ vectors $\phi_1, \phi_2, \ldots, \phi_n, \psi$ must be linearly dependent, so there must be scalars $a_1, a_2, \ldots, a_n, a_{n+1}$, not all zero, such that $a_1\phi_1 + a_2\phi_2 + \cdots + a_n\phi_n + a_{n+1}\psi = 0$. Since

---

[4] See Section 3, *Hilbert Space*.

$\phi_1, \phi_2, \ldots, \phi_n$ are not linearly dependent, a_{n+1} is not zero and

$$\psi = \left(\frac{-a_1}{a_{n+1}}\right)\phi_1 + \left(\frac{-a_2}{a_{n+1}}\right)\phi_2 + \cdots + \left(\frac{-a_n}{a_{n+1}}\right)\phi_n.$$

Thus the set of vectors $\phi_1, \phi_2, \ldots, \phi_n$ spans the space and is a basis. This completes the proof of the theorem.

We have shown in fact that in an n-dimensional linear space any set of n linearly independent vectors is a basis.

Consider again some of the examples cited above. The Euclidean space of example (i) is indeed n-dimensional. It has a basis of n vectors $\psi_1 = (1, 0, \ldots, 0), \psi_2 = (0, 1, \ldots, 0) \ldots, \psi_n = (0, 0, \ldots, 1)$. The space of oscillating functions of example (iv) is two-dimensional. It has a basis of two vectors ψ_1 and ψ_2 defined by

$$\psi_1(x) = \sin(\omega x) \quad \text{and} \quad \psi_2(x) = \cos(\omega x).$$

All of the other examples are infinite-dimensional spaces.

Suppose the set of vectors $\phi_1, \phi_2, \ldots, \phi_n$ is a basis for an n-dimensional linear space. Then each vector ψ in the space is a linear combination $\psi = \sum_{k=1}^{n} a_k \phi_k$. The coefficients a_k of this linear combination are unique; if we look for another linear combination $\psi = \sum_{k=1}^{n} b_k \phi_k$ we find that

$$0 = \psi - \psi = \sum_{k=1}^{n}(a_k - b_k)\phi_k,$$

which implies that $a_k - b_k = 0$ for all $k = 1, 2, \ldots, n$ since the vectors ϕ_k are linearly independent. The set of coefficients $(a_1, a_2, \ldots, a_n)$ is a vector in n-dimensional Euclidean space. Thus we have a one-to-one correspondence between the given n-dimensional space and n-dimensional Euclidean space. This correspondence is maintained by the operations of addition and scalar multiplication; if $\phi = \sum_{k=1}^{n} c_k \phi_k$ is another vector, corresponding to the vector $(c_1, c_2, \ldots, c_n)$ in Euclidean space, then $\psi + \phi = \sum_{k=1}^{n}(a_k + c_k)\phi_k$ corresponds to $(a_1 + c_1, a_2 + c_2, \ldots, a_n + c_n)$; a scalar multiple $b\psi = \sum_{k=1}^{n} ba_k \phi_k$ corresponds to $(ba_1, ba_2, \ldots, ba_n)$. Thus, as far as linear-space properties are concerned, every n-dimensional linear space is essentially the same as n-dimensional Euclidean space. Of course the explicit correspondence is different for different choices of basis vectors.

2. INNER PRODUCTS

To get analogs of lengths of vectors and angles between vectors in ordinary three-dimensional position space we generalize the concept of a dot product of two vectors.

Definitions. An *inner product* or *scalar product* for a linear space is an assignment to each pair of vectors ψ and ϕ of a scalar (ψ, ϕ) called the *inner* or *scalar product* of ψ and ϕ, with the properties that for any vectors ψ, ϕ, χ and scalar a

(i) $(\psi, \phi + \chi) = (\psi, \phi) + (\psi, \chi)$,

(ii) $(\psi, a\phi) = a(\psi, \phi)$,

(iii) $(\psi, \phi) = (\phi, \psi)^*$,

(iv) $(\psi, \psi) \geq 0$ with the equality holding only if $\psi = 0$.

The non-negative number $\|\psi\| = \sqrt{(\psi, \psi)}$ is called the *norm* or *length* of the vector ψ. Two vectors are *orthogonal* if their inner product is zero.

For example, n-dimensional Euclidean space has an inner product defined by $(\psi, \phi) = \sum_{k=1}^{n} x_k^* y_k$ for vectors $\psi = (x_1, x_2, \ldots, x_n)$ and $\phi = (y_1, y_2, \ldots, y_n)$. There is a similar inner product for the space l^2 of infinite sequences: if $\psi = (x_1, x_2, \ldots, x_k, \ldots)$ and $\phi = (y_1, y_2, \ldots, y_k, \ldots)$, then $(\psi, \phi) = \sum_{k=1}^{\infty} x_k^* y_k$. The condition for l^2 that $\sum_{k=1}^{\infty} |x_k|^2$ is finite is just the requirement that $\|\psi\|$ is finite.[5]

For a space L^2 of square-integrable functions an inner product is defined by $(\psi, \phi) = \int \psi(x)^* \phi(x) \, dx$. The condition for a vector ψ in L_2 that $\int |\psi(x)|^2 \, dx$ is finite is again just the requirement that $\|\psi\|$ is finite. From this it can be shown that the inner product of any two vectors is finite.[6] If $\int |\psi(x) - \chi(x)|^2 \, dx$ is zero, the two functions $\psi(x)$ and $\chi(x)$ are taken to represent the same vector $\psi = \chi$ in L^2.[7] Then only the zero vector has zero length.

The fact that the cosine of an angle between two vectors never has magnitude greater then one finds its generalization in the following.

Theorem 2.1 (Schwarz's inequality). An inner product for a linear space has the property that for any two vectors ψ and ϕ

$$|(\psi, \phi)| \leq \|\psi\| \cdot \|\phi\|$$

with the equality holding if and only if ψ and ϕ are linearly dependent.

[5] That the inner product of two vectors is finite is shown by Cauchy's inequality $\sum_{k=1}^{n} |x_k^* y_k| \leq (\sum_{k=1}^{n} |x_k|^2)^{1/2} (\sum_{k=1}^{n} |y_k|^2)^{1/2}$ as $n \to \infty$. For each finite n this is Schwarz's inequality for n-dimensional Euclidean space applied to vectors which have the phases of their components adjusted so that $x_k^* y_k$ is positive for every k.
[6] See Riesz and Nagy, Section 21.
[7] Two such functions are equal "almost everywhere"; they differ only on a set of Lebesgue measure zero. Therefore they give the same result for any calculation where the function representing the vector is in an integral. See Riesz and Nagy, pp. 5–6 and Chapter 2.

Proof. If either vector is zero the theorem is satisfied rather trivially, so we need to consider only nonzero vectors. If we let $a = -(\phi, \psi)/(\phi, \phi)$ in the inequality

$$0 \le (\psi + a\phi, \psi + a\phi) = (\psi, \psi) + a(\psi, \phi) + a^*(\phi, \psi) + |a|^2 (\phi, \phi)$$

and multiply by (ϕ, ϕ), we get the desired inequality

$$0 \le (\psi, \psi)(\phi, \phi) - |(\psi, \phi)|^2.$$

The equality holds if and only if $\psi + a\phi = 0$, which is true if and only if ψ and ϕ are linearly dependent. This completes the proof.

The norm has the properties that for any vectors ψ and ϕ and scalar a

(i) $\|\psi\| \ge 0$ with the equality holding only if $\psi = 0$,
(ii) $\|a\psi\| = |a| \, \|\psi\|$,   (iii) $\|\psi + \phi\| \le \|\psi\| + \|\phi\|$.

In other words: (i) all vectors have positive lengths except the zero vector which has zero length; (ii) when a vector is multiplied by a scalar, the length of the vector is multiplied by the magnitude of the scalar; (iii) the triangle inequality: if ψ, ϕ, and $\psi + \phi$ are pictured as forming the sides of a triangle, then the length of the side $\psi + \phi$ is less than the sum of the lengths of the other two sides. The first two properties can be seen to follow rather directly from the definition. To establish the third property we use Schwarz's inequality to get

$$\begin{aligned}
\|\psi + \phi\|^2 &= \|\psi\|^2 + \|\phi\|^2 + 2 \operatorname{Re} (\psi, \phi) \\
&\le \|\psi\|^2 + \|\phi\|^2 + 2 \, |(\psi, \phi)| \\
&\le \|\psi\|^2 + \|\phi\|^2 + 2 \, \|\psi\| \, \|\phi\| = (\|\psi\| + \|\phi\|)^2.
\end{aligned}$$

Mutually orthogonal vectors of unit length are called *orthonormal*. If a set of vectors $\phi_1, \phi_2, \ldots, \phi_k, \ldots$ is orthonormal, then $(\phi_j, \phi_k) = \delta_{jk}$. An *orthonormal basis* for a finite-dimensional space is a basis which consists of orthonormal vectors. For example the basis exhibited above for n-dimensional Euclidean space is an orthonormal basis.

When a vector ψ is expanded as a linear combination $\psi = \sum_k a_k \phi_k$ of orthonormal basis vectors ϕ_k, the coefficients a_k are given by

$$(\phi_k, \psi) = \sum_j a_j (\phi_k, \phi_j) = \sum_j a_j \delta_{kj} = a_k.$$

Thus

$$\psi = \sum_k (\phi_k, \psi) \phi_k.$$

A similar calculation shows that if vectors $\phi_1, \phi_2, \ldots, \phi_n$ are all nonzero and mutually orthogonal, then they are linearly independent; if $a_1, a_2, \ldots, a_n$

are scalars such that $\sum_{j=1}^{n} a_j \phi_j = 0$, then

$$0 = \sum_{j=1}^{n} a_j(\phi_k, \phi_j) = a_k(\phi_k, \phi_k),$$

which implies that $a_k = 0$ for $k = 1, 2, \ldots, n$.

Let the set of vectors $\phi_1, \phi_2, \ldots, \phi_n$ be an orthonormal basis for an n-dimensional linear space. Consider again the one-to-one correspondence with n-dimensional Euclidean space which matches $\psi = \sum_{k=1}^{n} a_k \phi_k$ with $(a_1, a_2, \ldots, a_n)$. Because the basis vectors $\phi_1, \phi_2, \ldots, \phi_n$ are orthonormal, this correspondence preserves norms and inner products; if $\phi = \sum_{k=1}^{n} b_k \phi_k$ is another vector, corresponding to the vector $(b_1, b_2, \ldots, b_n)$ in Euclidean space, then

$$(\psi, \phi) = \sum_{j=1}^{n} \sum_{k=1}^{n} a_j^* b_k (\phi_j, \phi_k) = \sum_{j=1}^{n} \sum_{k=1}^{n} a_j^* b_k \delta_{jk} = \sum_{k=1}^{n} a_k^* b_k.$$

Thus, as far as linear-space and inner-product properties are concerned, any n-dimensional space can be identified with n-dimensional Euclidean space by use of an orthonormal basis.

An orthonormal basis can be constructed by the *Gram-Schmidt orthogonalization process*. Let the set of vectors $\psi_1, \psi_2, \ldots, \psi_n$ be a basis for an n-dimensional space. The Gram-Schmidt process constructs orthogonal basis vectors by subtracting from each vector ψ_k its components in the directions of the previously orthogonalized vectors. Thus, if we let $\phi_1 = \psi_1$ and $\phi_2 = a_1 \phi_1 + \psi_2$ with $a_1 = -(\phi_1, \psi_2)/(\phi_1, \phi_1)$, we get $(\phi_1, \phi_2) = 0$. We proceed by induction. Suppose we have constructed k mutually orthogonal vectors $\phi_1, \phi_2, \ldots, \phi_k$. We let $\phi_{k+1} = \sum_{j=1}^{k} a_j \phi_j + \psi_{k+1}$ with $a_j = -(\phi_j, \psi_{k+1})/(\phi_j, \phi_j)$ and get $(\phi_j, \phi_{k+1}) = 0$ for $j = 1, 2, \ldots, k$. We repeat this step until we have n mutually orthogonal vectors $\phi_1, \phi_2, \ldots, \phi_n$. At each step there are scalars b_j such that $\phi_{k+1} = \sum_{j=1}^{k} b_j \psi_j + \psi_{k+1}$. From this we see that ϕ_{k+1} is not zero; if ϕ_{k+1} were zero, the vectors $\psi_1, \psi_2, \ldots, \psi_{k+1}$ would be linearly dependent since the coefficient of ψ_{k+1} is not zero. Thus the mutually orthogonal vectors $\phi_1, \phi_2, \ldots, \phi_n$ are all nonzero and therefore are linearly independent. The set of vectors $(1/\|\phi_1\|)\phi_1, (1/\|\phi_2\|)\phi_2, \ldots, (1/\|\phi_n\|)\phi_n$ is an orthonormal basis.

3. HILBERT SPACE

To work in an infinite-dimensional space we need to know how to handle a linear combination of an infinite number of vectors. This is analogous to a sum $w = \sum_{k=1}^{\infty} z_k$ of an infinite series of complex numbers z_k. The sum is the complex number w if the sequence of partial sums $w_n = \sum_{k=1}^{n} z_k$

converges to w as $n \to \infty$. This convergence, $w_n \to w$, means that $|w - w_n| \to 0$ as $n \to \infty$. Convergence of a sequence of vectors ψ_n to a limit vector ψ, or $\psi_n \to \psi$, means that $\|\psi - \psi_n\| \to 0$ as $n \to \infty$. An infinite linear combination $\sum_{k=1}^{\infty} a_k \phi_k$ is defined if the sequence of partial sums $\psi_n = \sum_{k=1}^{n} a_k \phi_k$ converges; then $\psi = \sum_{k=1}^{\infty} a_k \phi_k$ means that $\psi_n \to \psi$. This definition depends on the fact that the limit of a convergent sequence of vectors is a uniquely specified vector; if $\psi_n \to \psi$ and $\psi_n \to \chi$, then $\psi - \chi$ must be zero since

$$\|\psi - \chi\| = \|\psi - \psi_n + \psi_n - \chi\| \leq \|\psi - \psi_n\| + \|\psi_n - \chi\|$$

can be made smaller than any positive number by choosing n large enough.

Infinite linear combinations can be added componentwise just as finite linear combinations. If $\psi = \sum_{k=1}^{\infty} a_k \phi_k$ and $\chi = \sum_{k=1}^{\infty} b_k \phi_k$, then $\psi + \chi = \sum_{k=1}^{\infty} (a_k + b_k) \phi_k$; if the sequence of partial sums $\psi_n = \sum_{k=1}^{n} a_k \phi_k$ converges to ψ and the sequence of partial sums $\chi_n = \sum_{k=1}^{n} b_k \phi_k$ converges to χ, then the sequence of partial sums $\psi_n + \chi_n = \sum_{k=1}^{n} (a_k + b_k) \phi_k$ converges to $\psi + \chi$ since $\|\psi + \chi - (\psi_n + \chi_n)\| \leq \|\psi - \psi_n\| + \|\chi - \chi_n\|$.

Multiplication of an infinite linear combination by a scalar also can be done componentwise. If $\psi = \sum_{k=1}^{\infty} a_k \phi_k$, then $b\psi = \sum_{k=1}^{\infty} ba_k \phi_k$; if $\sum_{k=1}^{\infty} a_k \phi_k = \psi_n \to \psi$, then $\sum_{k=1}^{n} ba_k \phi_k = b\psi_n \to b\psi$ since $\|b\psi - b\psi_n\| = |b| \, \|\psi - \psi_n\|$.

A closed set in the complex plane has the property that if a sequence of complex numbers z_n in the set converges, $z_n \to z$, then its limit point z also is in the set. A *closed* set of vectors is defined by the same property; if a sequence of vectors ψ_n in the set converges, $\psi_n \to \psi$, then the limit vector ψ also is in the set.

A closed linear manifold is called a *subspace*. If a linear manifold contains vectors $\phi_1, \phi_2, \ldots, \phi_k, \ldots$, then it contains all finite linear combinations $\sum_{k=1}^{n} a_k \phi_k$; if the linear manifold is a subspace, then it also contains all infinite linear combinations $\sum_{k=1}^{\infty} a_k \phi_k$ since it contains the limits of sequences of partial sums. We say that a set of orthonormal vectors $\phi_1, \phi_2, \ldots, \phi_k, \ldots$ *spans* an infinite-dimensional subspace and is an *orthonormal basis* for the subspace, if each vector ψ in the subspace is a linear combination $\psi = \sum_{k=1}^{\infty} a_k \phi_k$, with infinite as well as finite linear combinations being counted. In particular the whole vector space is closed and is therefore a subspace, since convergence of a sequence of vectors is defined only as convergence to a limit vector in the space.

The previous sentence avoids an important question: Is there a limit vector in the space for every sequence of vectors which should converge or do some sequences of vectors fail to converge only because their limit vectors have been left out? Well, which sequences of vectors should converge? A sequence of complex numbers z_n converges if it is a Cauchy sequence—that is, if $|z_n - z_m| \to 0$ as $m, n \to \infty$. A sequence of vectors ψ_n is called a *Cauchy sequence* if $\|\psi_n - \psi_m\| \to 0$ as $m, n \to \infty$. Every sequence of vectors which converges to a limit is a Cauchy sequence; if $\psi_n \to \psi$, then

$$\|\psi_n - \psi_m\| = \|\psi_n - \psi + \psi - \psi_m\| \leq \|\psi_n - \psi\| + \|\psi - \psi_m\| \to 0$$

as $m, n \to \infty$. Conversely, every Cauchy sequence "should" converge. A space is said to be *complete* if every Cauchy sequence of vectors converges to a limit vector in the space. If a linear space with an inner product is complete, it is called a *Hilbert space*.

A Hilbert space is *separable* if it has an orthonormal basis which consists of a countable (finite or infinite) number of vectors, say $\phi_1, \phi_2, \phi_3, \ldots$. Then every orthonormal basis is countable.[8]

Every finite-dimensional space is complete. Let the set of vectors $\phi_1, \phi_2, \ldots, \phi_n$ be an orthonormal basis for an n-dimensional space. If the sequence of vectors $\psi_m = \sum_{k=1}^{n} a_k{}^m \phi_k$ is Cauchy, so that

$$\|\psi_m - \psi_l\|^2 = \sum_{k=1}^{n} |a_k{}^m - a_k{}^l|^2 \to 0$$

as $l, m \to \infty$, then for each $k = 1, 2, \ldots, n$ the sequence of scalars $a_k{}^m$ is Cauchy because $|a_k{}^m - a_k{}^l| \to 0$ as $l, m \to \infty$. Because the real or complex numbers are complete, each Cauchy sequence of scalars $a_k{}^m$ has a limit a_k. The sequence of vectors ψ_m converges to the limit vector $\psi = \sum_{k=1}^{n} a_k \phi_k$; because $a_k{}^m \to a_k$,

$$\|\psi - \psi_m\|^2 = \sum_{k=1}^{n} |a_k - a_k{}^m|^2 \to 0$$

as $m \to \infty$. Thus the space is complete. This also shows that a finite-dimensional linear manifold is closed; if a sequence of vectors in the manifold converges to a limit, then it is a Cauchy sequence and the limit vector is in the manifold. Every finite-dimensional space is a separable Hilbert space (Theorem 1.1). Every finite-dimensional linear manifold is a subspace.

An example of an infinite-dimensional Hilbert space is the space l^2 of infinite sequences $(x_1, x_2, \ldots, x_k, \ldots)$ such that $\sum_{k=1}^{\infty} |x_k|^2$ is finite. The important fact is that l^2 is complete, but because the proof of this fact is not very instructive, we omit it.[9] The space l^2 is a separable Hilbert space. It has an orthonormal basis consisting of the vectors $\phi_1 = (1, 0, 0, 0, \ldots)$, $\phi_2 = (0, 1, 0, 0, \ldots)$, $\phi_3 = (0, 0, 1, 0, \ldots)$, and so forth. Each vector $\psi = (x_1, x_2, \ldots, x_k, \ldots)$ in l^2 is a linear combination $\psi = \sum_{k=1}^{\infty} x_k \phi_k$; the

[8] We have skipped the definition that a separable space is one which contains a countable dense set of vectors and the proof that an orthonormal basis is countable; see Riesz and Nagy, Sections 32 and 33.
[9] See, for example, M. A. Naimark, *Normed Rings*, translated by L. F. Boron (P. Noordhoff, Ltd., Groningen, 1960), pp. 70–71.

sequence of partial sums $\psi_n = \sum_{k=1}^{n} x_k \phi_k$ converges to ψ since $\psi_n = (x_1, x_2, \ldots, x_n, 0, 0, \ldots)$ and $\psi - \psi_n = (0, 0, \ldots, 0, x_{n+1}, x_{n+2}, \ldots)$ so $\|\psi - \psi_n\|^2 = \sum_{k=n+1}^{\infty} |x_k|^2$ must converge to zero as $n \to \infty$ because $\sum_{k=1}^{\infty} |x_k|^2$ is finite.

Suppose that the set of vectors $\phi_1, \phi_2, \ldots, \phi_k, \ldots$ is an orthonormal basis for an infinite-dimensional separable Hilbert space. Then each vector ψ in the space is a linear combination $\psi = \sum_{k=1}^{\infty} a_k \phi_k$. The coefficients of this linear combination are unique; they are the inner products $a_k = (\phi_k, \psi)$. Thus $\psi = \sum_{k=1}^{\infty} (\phi_k, \psi)\phi_k$ just as for a finite linear combination. To prove this we use the sequence of partial sums $\psi_n = \sum_{k=1}^{n} a_k \phi_k$ which converges to ψ and evaluate the inner products $(\phi_k, \psi_n) = 0$ if $n < k$ and $(\phi_k, \psi_n) = a_k$ if $n \geq k$. The inner product (ϕ_k, ψ) is the limit as $n \to \infty$ of (ϕ_k, ψ_n) which is a_k. Here we use the fact that if a sequence of vectors ψ_n converges to a limit vector ψ then for any vector χ the sequence of inner products (χ, ψ_n) converges to (χ, ψ); by Schwarz's inequality

$$|(\chi, \psi) - (\chi, \psi_n)| = |(\chi, \psi - \psi_n)| \leq \|\chi\| \, \|\psi - \psi_n\| \to 0$$

as $n \to \infty$.

If $\psi = \sum_{k=1}^{\infty} a_k \phi_k$ and $\phi = \sum_{k=1}^{\infty} b_k \phi_k$ in terms of the orthonormal basis vectors ϕ_k, then $(\psi, \phi) = \sum_{k=1}^{\infty} a_k^* b_k$. This can be proved by a double application of the convergence of inner products used in the preceding paragraph. In particular $\|\psi\|^2 = \sum_{k=1}^{\infty} |a_k|^2$. Since $\|\psi\|$ is finite, $\sum_{k=1}^{\infty} |a_k|^2$ is finite and ψ can be identified with the vector $(a_1, a_2, \ldots, a_k, \ldots)$ in l^2. With this identification addition, scalar multiplication, and inner products all are the same as for l^2.

For each vector $(x_1, x_2, \ldots, x_k, \ldots)$ in l^2 is there a vector $\chi = \sum_{k=1}^{\infty} x_k \phi_k$ in the separable Hilbert space spanned by the orthonormal basis vectors ϕ_k? There is because the Hilbert space is complete. The sequence of partial sums $\chi_n = \sum_{k=1}^{n} x_k \phi_k$ is a Cauchy sequence since $\|\chi_n - \chi_m\|^2 = \sum_{k=m+1}^{n} |x_k|^2$ for $m < n$ and the convergence of this to zero as $m, n \to \infty$ is just the statement that the sequence of partial sums $\sum_{k=1}^{n} |x_k|^2$ is a Cauchy sequence, as it must be since $\sum_{k=1}^{\infty} |x_k|^2$ is finite. Because the space is complete, the Cauchy sequence of vectors χ_n converges to a limit vector $\chi = \sum_{k=1}^{\infty} x_k \phi_k$. Thus any infinite-dimensional separable Hilbert space can be identified with l^2.

A space L^2 of square-integrable functions is a separable Hilbert space. Again we omit the proofs.[10] For an example of an orthonormal basis consider the space $L^2(0, 1)$ of square-integrable functions $\psi(x)$ on the interval $0 \leq x \leq 1$. The set of functions 1, $\sqrt{2} \cos 2\pi k x$, and $\sqrt{2} \sin 2\pi k x$ for $k = 1, 2, 3, \ldots$ is a set of orthonormal vectors in $L^2(0, 1)$. According to the theory of Fourier

---

[10] See Riesz and Nagy, Sections 28, 32, and 33.

series[11] this is an orthonormal basis. If $\int_0^1 |\psi(x)|^2 \, dx$ is finite, then

$$\psi(x) = a_0 + \sum_{k=1}^{\infty} a_k \sqrt{2} \cos 2\pi k x + \sum_{k=1}^{\infty} b_k \sqrt{2} \sin 2\pi k x$$

with

$$a_0 = \int_0^1 \psi(x) \, dx, \qquad a_k = \int_0^1 \sqrt{2} \cos 2\pi k x \; \psi(x) \, dx,$$

$$b_k = \int_0^1 \sqrt{2} \sin 2\pi k x \; \psi(x) \, dx,$$

in the sense that the sequence of partial sums ψ_n defined by

$$\psi_n(x) = a_0 + \sum_{k=1}^{n} a_k \sqrt{2} \cos 2\pi k x + \sum_{k=1}^{n} b_k \sqrt{2} \sin 2\pi k x$$

converges to ψ. This means that

$$\| \psi - \psi_n \|^2 = \int_0^1 |\psi(x) - \psi_n(x)|^2 \, dx$$

converges to zero as $n \to \infty$. We have an orthonormal basis of continuous functions. This shows that there is no Hilbert space which is smaller than $L^2(0, 1)$ and contains the continuous square-integrable functions on the interval $0 \leq x \leq 1$; every Lebesgue-square-integrable function is a linear combination of continuous functions.

A subspace of a separable Hilbert space is a separable Hilbert space. It is clearly a Hilbert space; every Cauchy sequence of vectors in the subspace converges to a limit, and the limit must be in the subspace because the subspace is closed. That the subspace is separable is easy to accept intuitively but a bit complicated for us to prove, so we omit the proof.[12]

Let $\mathcal{M}$ be a subspace of a separable Hilbert space. The set of all vectors which are orthogonal to every vector in $\mathcal{M}$ is called the *orthogonal complement* $\mathcal{M}^{\perp}$ of $\mathcal{M}$. Evidently $\mathcal{M}^{\perp}$ is a linear manifold; if ψ and ϕ are vectors in $\mathcal{M}^{\perp}$ and a is a scalar, then for any vector χ in $\mathcal{M}$

$$(\chi, \psi + \phi) = (\chi, \psi) + (\chi, \phi) = 0$$

and

$$(\chi, a\psi) = a(\chi, \psi) = 0$$

so $\psi + \phi$ and $a\psi$ are in $\mathcal{M}^{\perp}$. In fact $\mathcal{M}^{\perp}$ is a subspace; if a sequence of vectors

[11] G. H. Hardy and W. W. Rogosinski, *Fourier Series* (Cambridge University Press, 1950).
[12] See footnote 8 and M. H. Stone, *Linear Transformations in Hilbert Space* (American Mathematical Society, New York, 1932), Theorem 1.19.

ψ_n in $\mathcal{M}^\perp$ converges to a limit vector ψ, then for any vector χ in $\mathcal{M}$ the inner product (χ, ψ) is the limit as $n \to \infty$ of (χ, ψ_n) which is zero, so ψ is in $\mathcal{M}^\perp$.

Let the set of vectors $\psi_1, \psi_2, \ldots, \psi_k, \ldots$ be an orthonormal basis for $\mathcal{M}$. For any vector ψ

$$\sum_k |(\psi_k, \psi)|^2 \leq \|\psi\|^2$$

is finite. Thus, because $\mathcal{M}$ is complete,

$$\psi_{\mathcal{M}} = \sum_k (\psi_k, \psi)\psi_k$$

is a vector in $\mathcal{M}$. Let $\psi_{\mathcal{M}^\perp} = \psi - \psi_{\mathcal{M}}$. Then $(\psi_k, \psi_{\mathcal{M}^\perp}) = 0$ for all of the orthonormal basis vectors ψ_k of $\mathcal{M}$ so $\psi_{\mathcal{M}^\perp}$ is in $\mathcal{M}^\perp$. We have got $\psi = \psi_{\mathcal{M}} + \psi_{\mathcal{M}^\perp}$ as a sum of a vector in $\mathcal{M}$ and a vector in $\mathcal{M}^\perp$. There is only one way to do this; because $(\psi_k, \psi_{\mathcal{M}^\perp})$ must be zero, the only possibility is that $(\psi_k, \psi_{\mathcal{M}}) = (\psi_k, \psi)$ for each of the orthonormal basis vectors ψ_k of $\mathcal{M}$. We refer to $\psi_{\mathcal{M}}$ as the *projection* of ψ on $\mathcal{M}$.

For example, suppose the set of vectors $\phi_0, \phi_1, \phi_2, \ldots, \psi_1, \psi_2, \ldots$ is an orthonormal basis for a separable Hilbert space. For $L^2(0, 1)$ these vectors could be $\phi_0(x) = 1$, $\phi_k(x) = \sqrt{2} \cos 2\pi kx$, and $\psi_k(x) = \sqrt{2} \sin 2\pi kx$ for $k = 1, 2, \ldots$. Let $\mathcal{M}$ be the set of all linear combinations $\sum_{k=1}^\infty a_k\psi_k$. Then $\mathcal{M}^\perp$ is the set of all linear combinations $\sum_{k=0}^\infty b_k\phi_k$.

Two subspaces $\mathcal{M}$ and $\mathcal{N}$ are called *orthogonal* if every vector in $\mathcal{M}$ is orthogonal to every vector in $\mathcal{N}$; for example, $\mathcal{M}$ and $\mathcal{M}^\perp$ are orthogonal. Let $\mathcal{M}_1, \mathcal{M}_2, \ldots, \mathcal{M}_k, \ldots$ be subspaces of a Hilbert space $\mathcal{H}$. We say that $\mathcal{H}$ is the *direct sum* of these subspaces and write $\mathcal{H} = \mathcal{M}_1 \oplus \mathcal{M}_2 \ldots \oplus \mathcal{M}_k \ldots$ or $\mathcal{H} = \sum_k \oplus \mathcal{M}_k$ if the subspaces $\mathcal{M}_k$ are mutually orthogonal and each vector in $\mathcal{H}$ is equal to the sum of its projections on these subspaces. For example, if $\mathcal{M}$ is a subspace of $\mathcal{H}$, then $\mathcal{H} = \mathcal{M} \oplus \mathcal{M}^\perp$.

4. LINEAR FUNCTIONALS

Linear scalar-valued functions of vectors are called *linear functionals*. A linear functional F assigns a scalar $F(\phi)$ to each vector ϕ such that for any vectors ϕ and ψ and scalar a

$$F(\phi + \psi) = F(\phi) + F(\psi)$$

and

$$F(a\phi) = aF(\phi).$$

Linear functionals form a linear space with the sum $F_1 + F_2$ of two linear functionals F_1 and F_2 and the scalar multiple aF of a linear functional F and scalar a defined by

$$(F_1 + F_2)(\phi) = F_1(\phi) + F_2(\phi)$$

and

$$(aF)(\phi) = aF(\phi)$$

for every vector ϕ.

For a space with an inner product a linear functional F_ψ is defined for each vector ψ by letting $F_\psi(\phi) = (\psi, \phi)$ for every vector ϕ. Sums and scalar multiples of these linear functionals are determined by the properties of the inner product; for any vectors ψ and χ and scalar a

$$F_\psi + F_\chi = F_{(\psi+\chi)}$$

and

$$aF_\psi = F_{a*\psi}.$$

Let the set of vectors $\phi_1, \phi_2, \ldots, \phi_n$ be an orthonormal basis for an n-dimensional vector space. To each linear functional F on this space we assign the vector

$$\psi_F = \sum_{k=1}^{n} F(\phi_k)^* \phi_k.$$

Then for any vector $\phi = \sum_{k=1}^{n} (\phi_k, \phi)\phi_k$ we have

$$F(\phi) = \sum_{k=1}^{n} (\phi_k, \phi)F(\phi_k) = (\psi_F, \phi).$$

Thus every linear functional is of the kind described in the previous paragraph. We have a one-to-one correspondence between linear functionals and vectors.

To get a similar result for infinite-dimensional spaces we need the concept of continuity. A function f of a complex variable z is continuous if $f(z_n) \rightarrow f(z)$ whenever $z_n \rightarrow z$. The same property defines continuity for linear functionals; a linear functional F is *continuous* if $F(\chi_n)$ converges to $F(\chi)$ for any sequence of vectors χ_n which converges to a limit vector χ. A linear functional F_ψ defined by $F_\psi(\chi) = (\psi, \chi)$ is continuous; if $\chi_n \rightarrow \chi$ then $(\psi, \chi_n) \rightarrow (\psi, \chi)$. Thus for a finite-dimensional space every linear functional is continuous. For an infinite-dimensional space continuity is what is needed to extend the linearity to infinite linear combinations. If F is a continuous linear functional and $\chi = \sum_{k=1}^{\infty} a_k\phi_k$, then $F(\chi) = \sum_{k=1}^{\infty} a_k F(\phi_k)$; because F is continuous and the sequence of partial sums $\chi_n = \sum_{k=1}^{n} a_k\phi_k$ converges to χ, the sequence of partial sums $F(\chi_n) = \sum_{k=1}^{n} a_k F(\phi_k)$ must converge to $F(\chi)$. The usefulness of continuous linear functionals depends on this and the following.

Theorem 4.1. For each continuous linear functional F on a separable Hilbert space there is a unique vector ψ_F in the space such that $F(\phi) = (\psi_F, \phi)$ for every vector ϕ.

Proof. Let the set of vectors $\phi_1, \phi_2, \ldots, \phi_k, \ldots$ be an orthonormal basis. If there is such a vector ψ_F, then it is unique and we know what it is; if $F(\phi_k) = (\psi_F, \phi_k)$ for every basis vector ϕ_k, then

$$\psi_F = \sum_{k=1}^{\infty} F(\phi_k)^* \phi_k.$$

On the other hand, if this infinite linear combination converges to a vector ψ_F, then for any vector $\phi = \sum_{k=1}^{\infty} (\phi_k, \phi)\phi_k$ we have

$$F(\phi) = \sum_{k=1}^{\infty} (\phi_k, \phi) F(\phi_k) = (\psi_F, \phi)$$

so this vector ψ_F does the job. We did all this before for a finite-dimensional space. For an infinite-dimensional space the question is whether the infinite linear combination $\sum_{k=1}^{\infty} F(\phi_k)^* \phi_k$ defines a vector. It does if $\sum_{k=1}^{\infty} |F(\phi_k)|^2$ is finite. This is what we have to prove. Let $\psi_n = \sum_{k=1}^{n} F(\phi_k)^* \phi_k$. Then

$$F(\psi_n) = \sum_{k=1}^{n} |F(\phi_k)|^2 = \|\psi_n\|^2.$$

We want to show that this remains finite as $n \to \infty$. Let $\chi_n = (1/\|\psi_n\|^2)\psi_n$. Then $\|\chi_n\| = 1/\|\psi_n\|$ and $F(\chi_n) = 1$. But $F(0) = 0$, because F is linear. Therefore the continuity of F would be violated if $\chi_n \to 0$ as $n \to \infty$. Since F is continuous we conclude that $\|\chi_n\|$ does not converge to zero and $\|\psi_n\|$ does not become infinite, as $n \to \infty$. This completes the proof of the theorem.

Thus we have a one-to-one correspondence between continuous linear functionals and vectors.

In Dirac's notation[13] a vector ψ is written as $|\psi\rangle$ and an inner product (ψ, ϕ) as $\langle \psi \mid \phi \rangle$. The linear functional F_ψ defined by $F_\psi(\phi) = (\psi, \phi)$ is denoted by $\langle \psi |$ and $F_\psi(\phi)$ by $\langle \psi \mid \phi \rangle$. The correspondence between linear functionals and vectors via the inner product is built into this notation. There is nothing to distinguish the value of the linear functional $\langle \psi |$ for the vector $|\phi\rangle$ from the inner product of the vectors $|\psi\rangle$ and $|\phi\rangle$; they are both $\langle \psi \mid \phi \rangle$.

[13] P. A. M. Dirac, *The Principles of Quantum Mechanics*, Fourth Edition (Oxford University Press, 1958).

2

LINEAR OPERATORS

In quantum mechanics physical quantities are represented by linear operators on a vector space. Thus we are interested in vector spaces largely as the places where linear operators are defined. We will assume that the operators are defined on a separable Hilbert space; this is generally what is done in quantum mechanics.

5. OPERATORS AND MATRICES

A *linear operator* A on a vector space assigns to each vector ψ a vector $A\psi$ such that

$$A(\psi + \phi) = A\psi + A\phi$$

and

$$Aa\psi = aA\psi$$

for any vectors ψ and ϕ and scalar a. Two operators A and B are *equal*, $A = B$, if $A\psi = B\psi$ for every vector ψ. Linear operators form a linear space with the sum $A + B$ of two operators A and B and the scalar multiple aA of an operator A and scalar a defined by

$$(A + B)\psi = A\psi + B\psi$$

and

$$(aA)\psi = aA\psi$$

for every vector ψ.[1] The product AB of two linear operators A and B is defined by

$$(AB)\psi = A(B\psi)$$

for every vector ψ.

---

[1] This definition extends to infinite linear combinations; $A = \sum_{k=1}^{\infty} a_k B_k$ means that $A\psi = \sum_{k=1}^{\infty} a_k B_k \psi$ for every vector ψ.

The simplest example of a linear operator is the *identity* operator 1 which leaves every vector unchanged; it multiplies every vector by the scalar 1. A scalar multiple $b \cdot 1$ of the identity operator is the linear operator which multiplies every vector by the scalar b. We write just b for this operator $b \cdot 1$. Thus every scalar defines an operator. In particular the zero operator 0, which multiplies every vector by the scalar 0, has the property that $0\psi = 0$ for every vector ψ; for example, if $A = B$, then $A - B = 0$.

On a space of functions a linear operator A can be defined, for example, by

$$(A\psi)(x) = \frac{d\psi(x)}{dx}$$

or

$$(A\psi)(x) = \int a(x, y)\, \psi(y)\, dy.$$

On n-dimensional Euclidean space a linear operator A is defined by each $n \times n$ matrix of scalars a_{jk}: if $\psi = (x_1, x_2, \ldots, x_n)$, then $A\psi = (y_1, y_2, \ldots, y_n)$ with $y_j = \sum_{k=1}^{n} a_{jk}x_k$ for $j = 1, 2, \ldots, n$. On any n-dimensional vector space a linear operator A is defined by each $n \times n$ matrix of scalars a_{jk} in terms of basis vectors $\phi_1, \phi_2, \ldots, \phi_n$: if $\psi = \sum_{k=1}^{n} x_k\phi_k$, then $A\psi = \sum_{j=1}^{n} y_j\phi_j$ with $y_j = \sum_{k=1}^{n} a_{jk}x_k$. In particular $A\phi_k = \sum_{j=1}^{n} a_{jk}\phi_j$. Conversely, for any linear operator A on this space, each vector $A\phi_k$ is a linear combination of the basis vectors, and these linear combinations $A\phi_k = \sum_{j=1}^{n} a_{jk}\phi_j$ define a unique $n \times n$ matrix of scalars a_{jk}. This matrix has the property that if $\psi = \sum_{k=1}^{n} x_k\phi_k$, then

$$A\psi = \sum_{k=1}^{n} x_k A\phi_k = \sum_{k=1}^{n} x_k \sum_{j=1}^{n} a_{jk}\phi_j = \sum_{j=1}^{n} \left(\sum_{k=1}^{n} a_{jk}x_k \right)\phi_j = \sum_{j=1}^{n} y_j\phi_j$$

with $y_j = \sum_{k=1}^{n} a_{jk}x_k$. Thus we have a one-to-one correspondence between linear operators on an n-dimensional vector space and $n \times n$ matrices. The elements a_{jk} of the matrix corresponding to the operator A depend on the basis used to set up the correspondence. The only exceptions are scalar multiples of the identity operator; if $A = 1$, then $a_{jk} = \delta_{jk}$ for any basis. If the basis vectors $\phi_1, \phi_2, \ldots, \phi_n$ are orthonormal, then $a_{jk} = (\phi_j, A\phi_k)$ since

$$(\phi_j, A\phi_k) = \left(\phi_j, \sum_{i=1}^{n} a_{ik}\phi_i \right) = \sum_{i=1}^{n} a_{ik}(\phi_j, \phi_i) = \sum_{i=1}^{n} a_{ik}\delta_{ji} = a_{jk}.$$

Let a_{jk} and b_{jk} be the matrix elements corresponding to linear operators A and B. The matrix of sums $a_{jk} + b_{jk}$ corresponds to $A + B$. For a scalar b the matrix elements ba_{jk} correspond to bA. For the product AB we have

$$AB\phi_k = A \sum_{i=1}^{n} b_{ik}\phi_i = \sum_{i=1}^{n} b_{ik}A\phi_i = \sum_{i=1}^{n} b_{ik}\sum_{j=1}^{n} a_{ji}\phi_j = \sum_{j=1}^{n} \left(\sum_{i=1}^{n} a_{ji}b_{ik} \right)\phi_j$$

so the matrix elements corresponding to $C = AB$ are

$$c_{jk} = \sum_{i=1}^{n} a_{ji}b_{ik}.$$

This defines sums, scalar multiples, and products of matrices. Algebraic operations with linear operators often are done most easily in terms of matrices. (In particular one's fingers can be taught to do matrix multiplication.) The only noteworthy feature of this algebra is that multiplication is not commutative; AB may be different from BA.

6. BOUNDED OPERATORS

To extend the linearity of an operator to infinite linear combinations we need some continuity.

Definitions. A linear operator A is *continuous* if $A\psi_n \to A\psi$ for any sequence of vectors ψ_n which converges to a limit vector ψ. A linear operator A is *bounded* if there is a positive number b such that $\|A\psi\| \le b\,\|\psi\|$ for every vector ψ; the smallest number b with this property is called the *norm* of A and is denoted by $\|A\|$.

Theorem 6.1. A linear operator is continuous if and only if it is bounded.

Proof. Let A be a bounded linear operator. If a sequence of vectors ψ_n converges to a limit vector ψ, then

$$\|A\psi - A\psi_n\| = \|A(\psi - \psi_n)\| \le \|A\|\,\|\psi - \psi_n\| \to 0$$

so $A\psi_n \to A\psi$ as $n \to \infty$. Thus A is continuous.

Suppose a linear operator A is not bounded. For each positive integer n there must be a vector ψ_n such that $\|A\psi_n\| > n\,\|\psi_n\|$. Let $\chi_n = (1/n\,\|\psi_n\|)\psi_n$. Then $\|\chi_n\| = 1/n$ so $\chi_n \to 0$ as $n \to \infty$. But $\|A\chi_n\| > 1$ so $A\chi_n \nrightarrow 0$ as $n \to \infty$. Thus A is not continuous. This completes the proof of the theorem.

If A is a bounded linear operator and $\psi = \sum_{k=1}^{\infty} a_k\phi_k$, then $A\psi = \sum_{k=1}^{\infty} a_k A\phi_k$; if the sequence of partial sums $\psi_n = \sum_{k=1}^{n} a_k\phi_k$ converges to the limit vector ψ, then the sequence of partial sums $A\psi_n = \sum_{k=1}^{n} a_k A\phi_k$ converges to the limit vector $A\psi$.

Sums, scalar multiples, and products of bounded operators are bounded. In fact

$$\|A + B\| \le \|A\| + \|B\|$$
$$\|aA\| = |a|\,\|A\|$$
$$\|AB\| \le \|A\|\,\|B\|$$

for any bounded operators A and B and scalar a. The last property is evident from the definition. The first two are direct consequences of the same properties of the norm for vectors, as is the property that $\|A\| = 0$ if and only if $A = 0$. Thus the norm has the characteristic properties of a length for the linear space of operators.

A linear operator which multiplies every vector by the same scalar is bounded; if $A\psi = a\psi$ for every vector ψ, then $\|A\| = |a|$.

Every operator on a finite-dimensional space is bounded. Let A be a linear operator on an n-dimensional vector space and let the set of vectors $\phi_1, \phi_2, \ldots, \phi_n$ be an orthonormal basis. Let $a_{jk} = (\phi_j, A\phi_k)$ and let b be the largest of the numbers $|\sum_{i=1}^{n} a_{ij}^* a_{ik}|$ for $j, k = 1, 2, \ldots, n$. For any vector $\psi = \sum_{k=1}^{n} x_k \phi_k$ we have $A\psi = \sum_{j=1}^{n} y_j \phi_j$ with $y_j = \sum_{k=1}^{n} a_{jk} x_k$ and

$$\|A\psi\|^2 = \sum_{i=1}^{n} |y_i|^2 = \sum_{i=1}^{n} \sum_{j=1}^{n} a_{ij}^* x_j^* \sum_{k=1}^{n} a_{ik} x_k \leq \sum_{j=1}^{n} |x_j^*| \sum_{k=1}^{n} |x_k| \left| \sum_{i=1}^{n} a_{ij}^* a_{ik} \right|$$

$$\leq b \left(\sum_{k=1}^{n} |x_k| \right)^2 \leq bn^2 \sum_{k=1}^{n} |x_k|^2 = bn^2 \|\psi\|^2.$$

Thus A is bounded.

A bounded linear operator on an infinite-dimensional space can be represented by an infinite matrix. Let A be a bounded linear operator on a space for which the set of vectors $\phi_1, \phi_2, \ldots, \phi_k, \ldots$ is an orthonormal basis. The linear combinations $A\phi_k = \sum_{j=1}^{\infty} a_{jk} \phi_j$ define an infinite matrix of scalars $a_{jk} = (\phi_j, A\phi_k)$ for $j, k = 1, 2, \ldots$. If $\psi = \sum_{k=1}^{\infty} x_k \phi_k$ and $A\psi = \sum_{j=1}^{\infty} y_j \phi_j$, then $y_j = (\phi_j, A\psi)$, and because A is continuous $A\psi = \sum_{k=1}^{\infty} x_k A\phi_k$ so $(\phi_j, A\psi) = \sum_{k=1}^{\infty} x_k (\phi_j, A\phi_k)$ or $y_j = \sum_{k=1}^{\infty} a_{jk} x_k$. Thus A is represented by the matrix elements a_{jk}. The inverse problem of which infinite matrices represent bounded operators is much more complicated.[2]

7. INVERSES

We say that a linear operator A has an *inverse* if there is a linear operator B such that $BA = 1 = AB$. Some operators have inverses; others do not. No operator has more than one inverse; if B and C are inverses of A, then $BA = 1$ and $AB = 1 = AC$ so

$$B - C = BA(B - C) = B(AB - AC) = 0.$$

Thus if A has an inverse we can call it *the inverse* of A; we denote it by A^{-1}. What is required for an operator to have an inverse is clarified by the following.

[2] See, for example, A. E. Taylor, *Functional Analysis* (John Wiley and Sons, New York, 1958), Section 6.12.

Theorem 7.1. A linear operator A has an inverse if and only if for each vector ψ there is one and only one vector ϕ such that $\psi = A\phi$.

Proof. If A has an inverse A^{-1}, then for any vector ψ the vector $\phi = A^{-1}\psi$ has the property that $A\phi = AA^{-1}\psi = \psi$. If χ is a vector such that $A\chi = \psi$, then $\chi = A^{-1}A\chi = A^{-1}\psi$. This proves the "only if" part.

If for each vector ψ there is a unique vector ϕ such that $\psi = A\phi$, then we can define A^{-1} by letting $A^{-1}\psi = \phi$ for each vector ψ. We get $A^{-1}A = 1$ because $A^{-1}A\phi = \phi$ for any vector ϕ. (We assume that $A\phi$ is defined for every vector ϕ.) We get $AA^{-1} = 1$ because $AA^{-1}\psi = \psi$ for any vector ψ. We must show that A^{-1} is linear. For any two vectors ψ_1 and ψ_2 let $\psi_1 = A\phi_1$ and $\psi_2 = A\phi_2$. Then

$$A^{-1}(\psi_1 + \psi_2) = A^{-1}(A\phi_1 + A\phi_2) = A^{-1}A(\phi_1 + \phi_2)$$
$$= \phi_1 + \phi_2 = A^{-1}\psi_1 + A^{-1}\psi_2.$$

For any scalar a and vector $\psi = A\phi$

$$A^{-1}a\psi = A^{-1}aA\phi = A^{-1}Aa\phi = a\phi = aA^{-1}\psi.$$

This completes the proof of the theorem.

If a linear operator A has an inverse, then there is no nonzero vector ϕ such that $A\phi = 0$; if $A\phi = 0$ and A has an inverse A^{-1}, then $\phi = A^{-1}A\phi = 0$. Let the set of vectors $\phi_1, \phi_2, \ldots, \phi_n$ be linearly independent. If the linear operator A has an inverse, then the set of vectors $A\phi_1, A\phi_2, \ldots, A\phi_n$ is linearly independent; if $\sum_{k=1}^{n} b_k A\phi_k = 0$ and A has an inverse A^{-1}, then

$$\sum_{k=1}^{n} b_k \phi_k = A^{-1}\sum_{k=1}^{n} b_k A\phi_k = 0$$

so the scalars b_k all must be zero. We could have gotten either of these statements as a corollary to the preceding theorem instead of actually using the inverse.

For a finite-dimensional space the preceding are two of the statements which characterize an operator with an inverse.

Theorem 7.2. Let A be a linear operator on an n-dimensional vector space and let the set of vectors $\phi_1, \phi_2, \ldots, \phi_n$ be a basis. Each of the following is a necessary and sufficient condition for A to have an inverse.

(i) There is no nonzero vector ϕ such that $A\phi = 0$.
(ii) The set of vectors $A\phi_1, A\phi_2, \ldots, A\phi_n$ is linearly independent.
(iii) There is a linear operator B such that $BA = 1$.
(iv) The matrix corresponding to A has nonzero determinant.

Proof. We know already that (i), (ii), and (iii) are necessary conditions for A to have an inverse. We will show that (iii) implies (i), that (i) implies (ii), and that (ii) implies the existence of an inverse. If $BA = 1$ and $A\phi = 0$, then $\phi = BA\phi = 0$. Thus (iii) implies (i). If there is no nonzero vector $\sum_{k=1}^{n} a_k \phi_k$ such that $A \sum_{k=1}^{n} a_k \phi_k = 0$, then (because the vectors ϕ_k are linearly independent) there are no nonzero scalars a_k such that $\sum_{k=1}^{n} a_k A \phi_k = 0$. Thus (i) implies (ii). If the set of vectors $A\phi_1, A\phi_2, \ldots, A\phi_n$ is linearly independent, then it is a basis and for each vector ψ there is a unique set of scalars a_k such that $\psi = \sum_{k=1}^{n} a_k A\phi_k$, or one and only one vector $\sum_{k=1}^{n} a_k \phi_k$ such that $\psi = A \sum_{k=1}^{n} a_k \phi_k$. Thus (ii) implies that A has an inverse (Theorem 7.1).

That (iv) is true when A has an inverse is evident because the determinant of a product of matrices is the product of their determinants.[3] If the determinant of the matrix corresponding to A were zero, then the determinant of the matrix corresponding to $A^{-1}A = 1$ would be zero, which it is not. That (iv) implies the existence of an inverse is Cramer's rule[3], which states that if the determinant of the matrix of scalars a_{jk} is not zero then there is a unique solution for the x_k of the equations $y_j = \sum_{k=1}^{n} a_{jk} x_k$ for $j = 1, 2, \ldots, n$. Thus for any vector $\psi = \sum_{j=1}^{n} y_j \phi_j$ there is one and only one vector $\phi = \sum_{k=1}^{n} x_k \phi_k$ such that $\psi = A\phi$. This completes the proof of the theorem.

For an infinite-dimensional space (i), (ii), and (iii) are not sufficient conditions for A to have an inverse. Let A be the linear operator on l^2 which for $\phi = (x_1, x_2, x_3, \ldots)$ gives $A\phi = (0, x_1, x_2, \ldots)$. There is no nonzero vector ϕ such that $A\phi = 0$. Consider the basis vectors $\phi_1 = (1, 0, 0, \ldots)$, $\phi_2 = (0, 1, 0, \ldots)$, and so forth. The set of vectors $A\phi_1, A\phi_2, \ldots$ is linearly independent. Let B be the linear operator on l^2 which for $\psi = (x_1, x_2, x_3, \ldots)$ gives $B\psi = (x_2, x_3, x_4, \ldots)$. Then $BA = 1$. But A has no inverse. If $\psi = (x_1, x_2, x_3, \ldots)$ with x_1 not zero, then there is no vector ϕ such that $\psi = A\phi$.

If linear operators A and B have inverses A^{-1} and B^{-1}, then AB has an inverse $(AB)^{-1} = B^{-1}A^{-1}$ since

$$B^{-1}A^{-1}AB = B^{-1}B = 1$$

and

$$ABB^{-1}A^{-1} = AA^{-1} = 1.$$

8. UNITARY OPERATORS

Among operators with inverses, those which leave the lengths of vectors unchanged are especially useful in quantum mechanics. They are the analogs of rotations in real three-dimensional space.

---

[3] G. Birkhoff and S. MacLane, *A Survey of Modern Algebra* (The Macmillan Co., New York, 1965), pp. 285–286.

Definition. A linear operator U is *unitary*[4] if it has an inverse and if $\|U\psi\| = \|\psi\|$ for every vector ψ.

For a finite-dimensional space the condition that $\|U\psi\| = \|\psi\|$ for every vector ψ implies that U has an inverse (Theorem 7.2); it shows that there is no nonzero vector ψ such that $U\psi = 0$. For an infinite-dimensional space this condition does not imply that U has an inverse. In the example above the operator A on l^2 which for $\psi = (x_1, x_2, x_3, \ldots)$ gives $A\psi = (0, x_1, x_2, \ldots)$ satisfies the condition that $\|A\psi\| = \|\psi\|$ for every vector ψ, but A has no inverse.

Every unitary operator is bounded; in fact, if U is a unitary operator, then $\|U\| = 1$.

Theorem 8.1. If U is a unitary operator, then $(U\psi, U\phi) = (\psi, \phi)$ for any vectors ψ and ϕ.

Proof. Let $\chi = \psi + \phi$. Then

$$\|\chi\|^2 = \|\psi\|^2 + \|\phi\|^2 + 2\operatorname{Re}(\psi, \phi)$$

and

$$\|U\chi\|^2 = \|U\psi\|^2 + \|U\phi\|^2 + 2\operatorname{Re}(U\psi, U\phi).$$

We conclude that $\operatorname{Re}(U\psi, U\phi) = \operatorname{Re}(\psi, \phi)$. For a real linear space the inner products are real and the proof is complete. For a complex linear space we repeat the above with $\chi = \psi - i\phi$ to get the imaginary parts.

Corollary 8.2. If U is a unitary operator and the set of vectors $\phi_1, \phi_2, \ldots, \phi_k, \ldots$ is an orthonormal basis, then the set of vectors $U\phi_1, U\phi_2, \ldots, U\phi_k, \ldots$ also is an orthonormal basis.

Proof. That the vectors $U\phi_1, U\phi_2, \ldots, U\phi_k, \ldots$ are orthonormal and therefore linearly independent follows from the preceding theorem. For a finite-dimensional space this is sufficient to establish that they are a basis. For an infinite-dimensional space we note also that if $U^{-1}\psi = \sum_{k=1}^{\infty} a_k\phi_k$, then $\psi = UU^{-1}\psi = \sum_{k=1}^{\infty} a_k U\phi_k$; thus any vector ψ is a linear combination of the vectors $U\phi_k$.

Theorem 8.3. Let the set of vectors $\phi_1, \phi_2, \ldots, \phi_k, \ldots$ be an orthonormal basis. If U is a bounded linear operator such that the set of vectors $U\phi_1, U\phi_2, \ldots, U\phi_k, \ldots$ is an orthonormal basis, then U is unitary.

Proof. For any vector $\phi = \sum_k a_k\phi_k$ we have

$$U\phi = \sum_k a_k U\phi_k$$

---

[4] Unitary operators on a real linear space are often called *orthogonal*.

and
$$\|U\phi\|^2 = \sum_k |a_k|^2 = \|\phi\|^2.$$

For any vector ψ we have

$$\psi = \sum_k a_k U\phi_k = U \sum_k a_k \phi_k = U\phi$$

for one and only one vector $\phi = \sum_k a_k \phi_k$ so U has an inverse (Theorem 7.1).

Let the set of vectors $\phi_1, \phi_2, \ldots, \phi_k, \ldots$ be an orthonormal basis and let the set of vectors $\psi_1, \psi_2, \ldots, \psi_k, \ldots$ be another orthonormal basis. For any vector $\phi = \sum_k a_k \phi_k$ let $U\phi = \sum_k a_k \psi_k$. This defines a linear operator U which is bounded and unitary. Thus a unitary operator determines a change of orthonormal basis, and a change of orthonormal basis determines a unitary operator.

For example, consider the complex space $L^2(0, 1)$ of complex square-integrable functions $\psi(x)$ on the interval $0 \leq x \leq 1$. Let ω be a real number and let U be the linear operator defined on $L^2(0, 1)$ by $(U\psi)(x) = e^{i\omega x}\psi(x)$ for every vector ψ. Evidently U has an inverse U^{-1} defined by $(U^{-1}\psi)(x) = e^{-i\omega x}\psi(x)$ for every vector ψ. Also for any vector ψ

$$\|U\psi\|^2 = \int_0^1 |(U\psi)(x)|^2 \, dx = \int_0^1 |e^{i\omega x}\psi(x)|^2 \, dx = \int_0^1 |\psi(x)|^2 \, dx = \|\psi\|^2.$$

Thus U is unitary. The set of vectors ϕ_k defined by $\phi_k(x) = e^{i2\pi kx}$ for $k = 0, \pm 1, \pm 2, \ldots$ is an orthonormal basis. We have

$$(U\phi_k)(x) = e^{i(\omega + 2\pi k)x}.$$

The set of vectors $U\phi_k$ for $k = 0, \pm 1, \pm 2, \ldots$ is another orthonormal basis. If $\omega/2\pi$ is an integer, then $U\phi_k = \phi_{k+\omega/2\pi}$, and the change of basis is only a change of labels on the same set of basis vectors; in this case the matrix elements of U are simply

$$u_{jk} = (\phi_j, U\phi_k) = \delta_{j,k+\omega/2\pi}.$$

9. ADJOINTS, HERMITIAN OPERATORS

The *adjoint* $A^\dagger$ of a bounded linear operator A is defined by letting

$$(\phi, A^\dagger\psi) = (A\phi, \psi)$$

for all vectors ψ and ϕ. This requires a word of explanation. For each vector ψ a linear functional F is defined by $F(\phi) = (\psi, A\phi)$. This linear functional is continuous because A is bounded; if a sequence of vectors χ_n converges to a limit vector χ, then

$$|F(\chi) - F(\chi_n)| = |(\psi, A[\chi - \chi_n])| \leq \|\psi\| \, \|A\| \, \|\chi - \chi_n\| \to 0$$

as $n \to \infty$. This implies (Theorem 4.1) that there is a unique vector, which we call $A^\dagger \psi$, such that $F(\phi) = (A^\dagger \psi, \phi)$ or $(A^\dagger \psi, \phi) = (\psi, A\phi)$.

That $A^\dagger$ is a linear operator is evident from the definition. It is also bounded.

Theorem 9.1.   Let A be a bounded linear operator. Then $A^\dagger$ is a bounded linear operator and $\|A^\dagger\| = \|A\|$.

Proof.   From

$$\|A^\dagger \psi\|^2 = (\psi, AA^\dagger \psi) \leq \|\psi\| \, \|A\| \, \|A^\dagger \psi\|$$

we see that $\|A^\dagger \psi\| \leq \|A\| \, \|\psi\|$, which implies that $A^\dagger$ is bounded and that $\|A^\dagger\| \leq \|A\|$. Then from

$$\|A\psi\|^2 = (\psi, A^\dagger A\psi) \leq \|\psi\| \, \|A^\dagger\| \, \|A\psi\|$$

we see that $\|A\psi\| \leq \|A^\dagger\| \, \|\psi\|$, which implies that $\|A\| \leq \|A^\dagger\|$. This completes the proof of the theorem.

It is an easy exercise using the definition of the adjoint to check that

$$(A^\dagger)^\dagger = A$$
$$(A + B)^\dagger = A^\dagger + B^\dagger$$
$$(aA)^\dagger = a^* A^\dagger$$
$$(AB)^\dagger = B^\dagger A^\dagger$$

for any bounded operators A and B and scalar a.

For any vectors ψ and ϕ we have

$$(\phi, A^\dagger \psi) = (\psi, A\phi)^*.$$

In particular consider orthonormal basis vectors $\phi_1, \phi_2, \ldots, \phi_k, \ldots$ and consider the representation of a bounded linear operator A by the matrix elements $a_{jk} = (\phi_j, A\phi_k)$. The adjoint $A^\dagger$ is represented by the matrix elements

$$a_{jk}^\dagger = (\phi_j, A^\dagger \phi_k) = (\phi_k, A\phi_j)^* = a_{kj}^*.$$

This defines the adjoint of a matrix.

A bounded linear operator A is called *self-adjoint* or *Hermitian* if $A^\dagger = A$. A Hermitian operator A is characterized by the equation

$$(\phi, A\psi) = (A\phi, \psi)$$

or

$$(\phi, A\psi) = (\psi, A\phi)^*$$

holding for all vectors ψ and ϕ. In particular if A is Hermitian, then $(\psi, A\psi)$ is real for any vector ψ. In terms of the matrix elements $a_{jk} = (\phi_j, A\phi_k)$ with respect to an orthonormal basis of vectors $\phi_1, \phi_2, \ldots, \phi_k, \ldots$ a Hermitian operator A is characterized by the property that

$$a_{jk} = (\phi_j, A\phi_k) = (\phi_k, A\phi_j)^* = a_{kj}^*$$

for $j, k = 1, 2, \ldots$. This defines a Hermitian matrix.

For example, consider again the space $L^2(0, 1)$ of square-integrable functions $\psi(x)$ on the interval $0 \leq x \leq 1$. Let A be the linear operator defined on $L^2(0, 1)$ by $(A\psi)(x) = x\psi(x)$ for every vector ψ. For any vector ψ

$$\|A\psi\|^2 = \int_0^1 |(A\psi)(x)|^2 \, dx = \int_0^1 |x\psi(x)|^2 \, dx \leq \int_0^1 |\psi(x)|^2 \, dx = \|\psi\|^2.$$

Thus A is bounded and $\|A\| = 1$. For any vectors ψ and ϕ

$$(\phi, A\psi) = \int_0^1 \phi(x)^*(A\psi)(x) \, dx = \int_0^1 \phi(x)^* x\psi(x) \, dx = \int_0^1 [x\phi(x)]^* \psi(x) \, dx$$

$$= \int_0^1 (A\phi)(x)^* \psi(x) \, dx = (A\phi, \psi).$$

Thus A is Hermitian. Consider again the orthonormal basis vectors ϕ_k defined by $\phi_k(x) = e^{i2\pi kx}$ for $k = 0, \pm 1, \pm 2, \ldots$. The matrix elements of A with respect to this basis are

$$a_{jk} = (\phi_j, A\phi_k) = \int_0^1 e^{-i2\pi jx} x e^{i2\pi kx} \, dx$$

for $j, k = 0, \pm 1, \pm 2, \ldots$. Thus we get $a_{kk} = \frac{1}{2}$ and $a_{jk} = i/2\pi(j - k)$ for $j \neq k$, and we see that $a_{jk} = a_{kj}^*$.

On the space $L^2(-\infty, \infty)$ of square-integrable functions $\psi(x)$ for $-\infty < x < \infty$, we can define a bounded Hermitian operator V, for example, by setting $(V\psi)(x) = e^{-|x|}\psi(x)$ for every vector ψ. That V is bounded and Hermitian is shown by calculations similar to those of the previous example.

Theorem 9.2.   If A is a bounded linear operator which has a bounded inverse A^{-1}, then $A^\dagger$ has an inverse, namely $(A^\dagger)^{-1} = (A^{-1})^\dagger$.

Proof.   For any vectors ψ and ϕ

$$(\phi, (A^{-1})^\dagger A^\dagger \psi) = (A^{-1}\phi, A^\dagger \psi) = (AA^{-1}\phi, \psi) = (\phi, \psi)$$

and

$$(\phi, A^\dagger (A^{-1})^\dagger \psi) = (A\phi, (A^{-1})^\dagger \psi) = (A^{-1}A\phi, \psi) = (\phi, \psi),$$

so

$$(A^{-1})^\dagger A^\dagger = 1 = A^\dagger (A^{-1})^\dagger.$$

Corollary 9.3.   If A is a bounded Hermitian operator which has a bounded inverse A^{-1}, then A^{-1} is Hermitian.

Bounded linear operators on a complex vector space are related to bounded Hermitian operators as complex numbers are related to real numbers. For each bounded operator A let

$$\text{Re } A = \left(\frac{1}{2}\right)(A + A^\dagger)$$

and

$$\text{Im } A = \left(\frac{-i}{2}\right)(A - A^\dagger).$$

Then Re A and Im A are bounded Hermitian operators and

$$A = \text{Re } A + i \text{ Im } A.$$

If A is Hermitian, then Re $A = A$ and Im $A = 0$. Thus Hermitian operators are the analogs of real numbers. In the same sense unitary operators are the analogs of complex numbers of absolute value one.

Theorem 9.4. A linear operator U is unitary if and only if $U^\dagger U = 1 = UU^\dagger$.

Proof. If $U^\dagger U = 1 = UU^\dagger$, then U has an inverse, namely $U^{-1} = U^\dagger$, and for any vector ψ

$$\| U\psi \|^2 = (\psi, U^\dagger U\psi) = \|\psi\|^2.$$

Thus U is unitary. Conversely, if U is unitary, then (Theorem 8.1) for any vectors ψ and ϕ

$$(\phi, U^\dagger U\psi) = (U\phi, U\psi) = (\phi, \psi),$$

so $U^\dagger U = 1$. Therefore

$$U^\dagger - U^{-1} = (U^\dagger - U^{-1})UU^{-1} = (U^\dagger U - U^{-1}U)U^{-1} = 0.$$

This completes the proof of the theorem.

Thus, if U is unitary, then $U^\dagger = U^{-1}$ also is unitary.

By using the adjoint we can easily see the matrix product corresponding to the product of bounded operators on an infinite-dimensional space. Let A and B be bounded linear operators, $C = AB$, and the set of vectors $\phi_1, \phi_2, \ldots, \phi_k, \ldots$ an orthonormal basis. Let $a_{jk} = (\phi_j, A\phi_k)$, $b_{jk} = (\phi_j, B\phi_k)$, and $c_{jk} = (\phi_j, C\phi_k)$ for $j, k = 1, 2, \ldots$. Then

$$c_{jk} = (\phi_j, AB\phi_k) = (A^\dagger\phi_j, B\phi_k) = \sum_{i=1}^{\infty}(\phi_i, A^\dagger\phi_j)^*(\phi_i, B\phi_k)$$

$$= \sum_{i=1}^{\infty}(\phi_j, A\phi_i)(\phi_i, B\phi_k) = \sum_{i=1}^{\infty} a_{ji}b_{ik}$$

for $j, k = 1, 2, \ldots$. Here we have written the inner product of the vectors $A^\dagger\phi_j$ and $B\phi_k$ in terms of their components with respect to the basis vectors ϕ_i.

Let U be a bounded linear operator and let $u_{jk} = (\phi_j, U\phi_k)$ be its matrix elements with respect to an orthonormal basis. Evidently U is unitary if and only if (Theorem 9.4)

$$\sum_i u_{ij}^* u_{ik} = \delta_{jk} = \sum_i u_{ji} u_{ki}^*.$$

10. PROJECTION OPERATORS

Let $\mathcal{M}$ be a subspace of a separable Hilbert space. For each vector ψ there are unique vectors $\psi_{\mathcal{M}}$ in $\mathcal{M}$ and $\psi_{\mathcal{M}^\perp}$ in the orthogonal complement $\mathcal{M}^\perp$ of $\mathcal{M}$ such that $\psi = \psi_{\mathcal{M}} + \psi_{\mathcal{M}^\perp}$.[5] The *projection* operator $E_{\mathcal{M}}$ onto the subspace $\mathcal{M}$ is defined by letting $E_{\mathcal{M}}\psi = \psi_{\mathcal{M}}$ for each vector ψ. It is easy to see that $E_{\mathcal{M}}$ is a bounded linear operator; in fact, $\|E_{\mathcal{M}}\| = 1$ if $\mathcal{M}$ contains nonzero vectors. If ψ is in $\mathcal{M}$, then $E_{\mathcal{M}}\psi = \psi$. If ψ is in $\mathcal{M}^\perp$, then $E_{\mathcal{M}}\psi = 0$.[6] Evidently $1 - E_{\mathcal{M}}$ is the projection operator onto $\mathcal{M}^\perp$; for each vector ψ

$$(1 - E_{\mathcal{M}})\psi = \psi - \psi_{\mathcal{M}} = \psi_{\mathcal{M}^\perp}.$$

The identity operator 1 is the projection operator onto the whole space. The zero operator 0 is the projection operator onto the subspace which contains only the zero vector. The zero operator is the only projection operator whose norm is not one.

Theorem 10.1. A bounded linear operator E is a projection operator if and only if $E^2 = E = E^\dagger$; the subspace onto which E projects is the set of vectors $E\psi$ for all vectors ψ.

Proof. Let E be the projection operator onto a subspace $\mathcal{M}$. For each vector ψ

$$E^2\psi = E\psi_{\mathcal{M}} = \psi_{\mathcal{M}} = E\psi,$$

so $E^2 = E$. For any vectors ψ and ϕ

$$(\phi, E\psi) = (\phi_{\mathcal{M}} + \phi_{\mathcal{M}^\perp}, \psi_{\mathcal{M}}) = (\phi_{\mathcal{M}}, \psi_{\mathcal{M}}) = (\phi_{\mathcal{M}}, \psi_{\mathcal{M}} + \psi_{\mathcal{M}^\perp}) = (E\phi, \psi),$$

so $E^\dagger = E$. If ψ is in $\mathcal{M}$, then $\psi = E\psi$. If $\phi = E\psi$, then $\phi = \psi_{\mathcal{M}}$ is in $\mathcal{M}$. Thus $\mathcal{M}$ is the set of vectors $E\psi$ for all vectors ψ.

Let E be a bounded linear operator with the property that $E^2 = E = E^\dagger$. Let $\mathcal{M}$ be the set of vectors $E\psi$ for all vectors ψ. For any vectors $E\psi$ and

[5] See Section 3, *Hilbert Space*.
[6] From this it is evident that the identity operator 1 is the only projection operator which has an inverse.

$E\phi$ in $\mathcal{M}$ and scalar a

$$E\psi + E\phi = E(\psi + \phi)$$

and

$$aE\psi = Ea\psi$$

are in $\mathcal{M}$. Thus $\mathcal{M}$ is a linear manifold. If a sequence of vectors $E\psi_n$ in $\mathcal{M}$ converges to a limit vector χ, then

$$E\psi_n = EE\psi_n \rightarrow E\chi,$$

because E is continuous. The sequence of vectors $E\psi_n$ can have at most one limit vector. Therefore $\chi = E\chi$ and χ is in $\mathcal{M}$. Thus $\mathcal{M}$ is a subspace. For each vector ψ the vector $(1 - E)\psi$ is in $\mathcal{M}^\perp$, because

$$(E\phi, [1 - E]\psi) = (\phi, E[1 - E]\psi) = (\phi, [E - E^2]\psi) = 0$$

for every vector $E\phi$ in $\mathcal{M}$. We have $\psi = E\psi + (1 - E)\psi$ with $E\psi$ in $\mathcal{M}$ and $(1 - E)\psi$ in $\mathcal{M}^\perp$. The vectors $\psi_{\mathcal{M}}$ in $\mathcal{M}$ and $\psi_{\mathcal{M}^\perp}$ in $\mathcal{M}^\perp$ such that $\psi = \psi_{\mathcal{M}} + \psi_{\mathcal{M}^\perp}$ are unique. Therefore $E\psi = \psi_{\mathcal{M}}$. Thus E is the projection operator onto $\mathcal{M}$. This completes the proof of the theorem.

Let E_1 and E_2 be projection operators onto subspaces $\mathcal{M}_1$ and $\mathcal{M}_2$. We say that E_1 and E_2 are *orthogonal* if $\mathcal{M}_1$ and $\mathcal{M}_2$ are orthogonal. This situation is characterized by either $E_1E_2 = 0$ or $E_2E_1 = 0$; all vectors $E_1\psi$ in $\mathcal{M}_1$ are orthogonal to all vectors $E_2\phi$ in $\mathcal{M}_2$ if and only if either

$$(\psi, E_1E_2\phi) = (E_1\psi, E_2\phi) = 0$$

or

$$(\phi, E_2E_1\psi) = (E_2\phi, E_1\psi) = 0$$

for all vectors ψ and ϕ.

If $\mathcal{M}_1$ is contained in $\mathcal{M}_2$, we write $E_1 \leq E_2$ or $E_2 \geq E_1$. This situation is characterized by either $E_1E_2 = E_1$ or $E_2E_1 = E_1$. If $E_1 \leq E_2$, then $\|E_1\psi\| \leq \|E_2\psi\|$ for any vector ψ, because

$$(E_1\psi, E_2\psi) = (\psi, E_1E_2\psi) = (\psi, E_1\psi) = (\psi, E_1^2\psi) = \|E_1\psi\|^2$$

and

$$\|E_2\psi - E_1\psi\|^2 = \|E_2\psi\|^2 + \|E_1\psi\|^2 - 2\,\mathrm{Re}\,(E_1\psi, E_2\psi)$$
$$= \|E_2\psi\|^2 - \|E_1\psi\|^2.$$

Theorem 10.2.   Let E_1 and E_2 be projection operators onto subspaces $\mathcal{M}_1$ and $\mathcal{M}_2$.

  (i) If $E_1E_2 = E_2E_1$, then E_1E_2 is a projection operator and the subspace onto which it projects is the intersection of $\mathcal{M}_1$ and $\mathcal{M}_2$—that is, the set of all vectors which are in both $\mathcal{M}_1$ and $\mathcal{M}_2$.

 (ii) If E_1 and E_2 are orthogonal, then $E_1 + E_2$ is the projection operator onto $\mathcal{M}_1 \oplus \mathcal{M}_2$.

(iii) If $E_1 \leq E_2$, then $E_2 - E_1$ is a projection operator and the subspace onto which it projects is the orthogonal complement of $\mathcal{M}_1$ in $\mathcal{M}_2$—that is, the set of all vectors in $\mathcal{M}_2$ which are orthogonal to every vector in $\mathcal{M}_1$.

Proof. This is an easy exercise using the preceding theorem.

For an example of a projection operator consider the following. Let the set of vectors $\phi_0, \phi_1, \phi_2, \ldots, \psi_1, \psi_2, \ldots$ be an orthonormal basis. For $L^2(0, 1)$ these could be the functions $\phi_0(x) = 1$, $\phi_k(x) = \sqrt{2} \cos 2\pi k x$, and $\psi_k(x) = \sqrt{2} \sin 2\pi k x$ for $k = 1, 2, \ldots$, which we have considered before. Let E be the projection operator onto the subspace $\mathcal{M}$ of all linear combinations $\sum_{k=1}^{\infty} a_k \psi_k$. Then $E\psi_k = \psi_k$ for $k = 1, 2, \ldots$ and $E\phi_k = 0$ for $k = 0, 1, 2, \ldots$. The matrix elements of E with respect to this basis are all zero except $(\psi_k, E\psi_k) = 1$ for $k = 1, 2, \ldots$. For the sin and cos basis of $L^2(0, 1)$ evidently $E\psi$ is the odd part of a function ψ.

Another example is the linear operator E defined on $L^2(-\infty, \infty)$, for some real number r, by $(E\psi)(x) = \psi(x)$ if $x \leq r$ and $(E\psi)(x) = 0$ if $x > r$ for every vector ψ. For any vectors ψ and ϕ

$$(\phi, E\psi) = \int_{-\infty}^{r} \phi(x)^* \psi(x) \, dx = (E\phi, \psi),$$

so E is Hermitian. Clearly $E^2 = E$. Therefore E is a projection operator. It projects onto the subspace of all vectors ψ such that $\psi(x) = 0$ for $x > r$.

Consider the one-dimensional subspace spanned by a vector ϕ with $\|\phi\| = 1$. The projection operator E onto this subspace is defined by $E\psi = (\phi, \psi)\phi$ for every vector ψ. This is not changed if ϕ is multiplied by a scalar of absolute value one; it is the same for any vector of unit length in the one-dimensional subspace. In Dirac notation we write $|\phi\rangle\langle\phi|$ for the projection operator onto the one-dimensional subspace spanned by a vector ϕ of length one. Then it is impossible to forget that $|\phi\rangle\langle\phi| \, \psi = \langle\phi \mid \psi\rangle \, \phi$.

Let the set of vectors $\phi_1, \phi_2, \ldots, \phi_k, \ldots$ be an orthonormal basis. For each k let E_k be the projection operator onto the one-dimensional subspace spanned by ϕ_k. These projection operators are mutually orthogonal; $E_j E_k = \delta_{jk} E_k$ or in Dirac notation

$$|\phi_j\rangle\langle\phi_j \mid \phi_k\rangle\langle\phi_k| = \delta_{jk} |\phi_k\rangle\langle\phi_k|.$$

They have the completeness property that $\sum_k E_k = 1$; for any vector ψ

$$\psi = \sum_k (\phi_k, \psi)\phi_k = \sum_k E_k \psi.$$

In Dirac notation the completeness property $\sum_k |\phi_k\rangle\langle\phi_k| = 1$ provides a handy way to remember things; for example, using Dirac notation $A \, |\psi\rangle$ for

$A\psi$ and $\langle\phi|\,A\,|\psi\rangle$ for $(\phi,\,A\psi)$, we can write

$$\psi = \sum_k |\phi_k\rangle\langle\phi_k|\,\psi = \sum_k \langle\phi_k\,|\,\psi\rangle\phi_k$$

$$\langle\chi\,|\,\psi\rangle = \langle\chi|\sum_k |\phi_k\rangle\langle\phi_k\,|\,\psi\rangle = \sum_k \langle\chi\,|\,\phi_k\rangle\,\langle\phi_k\,|\,\psi\rangle$$

$$\langle\phi_j|\,A\,|\psi\rangle = \langle\phi_j|\,A\sum_k |\phi_k\rangle\langle\phi_k\,|\,\psi\rangle = \sum_k \langle\phi_j|\,A\,|\phi_k\rangle\,\langle\phi_k\,|\,\psi\rangle$$

$$A\phi_k = \sum_j |\phi_j\rangle\langle\phi_j|\,A\phi_k = \sum_j \langle\phi_j|\,A\,|\phi_k\rangle\phi_j$$

$$\langle\phi_j|\,AB\,|\phi_k\rangle = \langle\phi_j|\,A\sum_i |\phi_i\rangle\langle\phi_i|\,B\,|\phi_k\rangle = \sum_i \langle\phi_j|\,A\,|\phi_i\rangle\,\langle\phi_i|\,B\,|\phi_k\rangle.$$

11.   UNBOUNDED OPERATORS

In quantum mechanics we often work with operators which are not bounded. For an example of such an operator consider the space $L^2(-\infty,\,\infty)$ of square-integrable functions $\psi(x)$ for $-\infty < x < \infty$, and let Q be the linear operator defined by $(Q\psi)(x) = x\psi(x)$. This operator has the Hermitian property that

$$(\phi,\,Q\psi) = \int_{-\infty}^{\infty} \phi(x)^*x\,\psi(x)\,dx = \int_{-\infty}^{\infty} [x\,\phi(x)]^*\psi(x)\,dx = (Q\phi,\,\psi)$$

when the integrals converge. It is not bounded, because

$$\|Q\psi\|^2 = \int_{-\infty}^{\infty} |x\psi(x)|^2\,dx$$

can be any number of times larger than

$$\|\psi\|^2 = \int_{-\infty}^{\infty} |\psi(x)|^2\,dx.$$

In fact Q is not even defined for all vectors; there are vectors ψ for which $x\,\psi(x)$ does not define a vector because $\int_{-\infty}^{\infty} |x\,\psi(x)|^2\,dx$ is not finite.

It is impossible to define an unbounded Hermitian operator for all vectors. That this is a general fact is shown by the following.

Theorem 11.1.   If a linear operator A is defined for all vectors and if $(\phi,\,A\psi) = (A\phi,\,\psi)$ for all vectors ψ and ϕ, then A is bounded.[7]

This can be useful in showing that an operator is self-adjoint; if an operator A is defined everywhere on the space and if $(\phi,\,A\psi) = (A\phi,\,\psi)$ for all vectors

[7] See Riesz and Nagy, Section 114.

ψ and ϕ, then A is bounded, so $A^\dagger$ is defined and $A = A^\dagger$. On the other hand, an unbounded operator can not be defined as a self-adjoint operator for all vectors. The unbounded operators which are most useful in quantum mechanics are self-adjoint operators defined for a smaller number of vectors.[8]

The set of all vectors ψ for which $A\psi$ is defined is called the *domain* of the operator A. We can assume that this is a linear manifold; if $A\psi$ and $A\phi$ are defined, then

$$A(\psi + \phi) = A\psi + A\phi$$

and

$$Ab\psi = bA\psi$$

define $A(\psi + \phi)$ and $Ab\psi$.

Until now we have assumed that the domain of every operator being considered is the whole space. In the absence of this assumption some of our definitions have to be refined. Thus $A = B$ implies that A and B have the same domain. The domain of $A + B$ is the set of all vectors which are in both the domain of A and the domain of B. The domain of AB is the set of all vectors ψ in the domain of B such that $B\psi$ is in the domain of A. Suppose the domain of A contains the domain of B and on the domain of B the two operators are the same. Then we say that A is an *extension* of B.

A set of vectors, for example the domain of an operator, is called *dense* if for every vector ψ there is a sequence of vectors ψ_n in the set such that $\psi_n \to \psi$. If an operator A has a dense domain, we can define $A^\dagger$ as follows. The domain of $A^\dagger$ is the set of all vectors ψ for which there is a vector $A^\dagger\psi$ such that

$$(\phi, A^\dagger\psi) = (A\phi, \psi)$$

for every vector ϕ in the domain of A. This defines $A^\dagger\psi$. For suppose χ and χ' are vectors such that

$$(\phi, \chi) = (\phi, \chi')$$

for every vector ϕ in the domain of A. Then, because the domain of A is dense, there is a sequence of vectors ϕ_n such that $\phi_n \to \chi - \chi'$ and

$$(\phi_n, \chi - \chi') = 0.$$

Therefore $\chi - \chi' = 0$, because

$$(\phi_n, \chi - \chi') \to (\chi - \chi', \chi - \chi').$$

The domain of $A^\dagger$ is clearly a linear manifold, and $A^\dagger$ is a linear operator.

An operator A is called *symmetric* if it has a dense domain and

$$(\phi, A\psi) = (A\phi, \psi)$$

---

[8] It is not very useful to define an unbounded operator for all vectors by giving up the self-adjoint property, but it is always possible; see A. E. Taylor, Section 1.71.

for all vectors ψ and ϕ in its domain. Then $A^\dagger\psi$ is defined, and $A^\dagger\psi = A\psi$, for every vector ψ in the domain of A, so $A^\dagger$ is an extension of A. If $A^\dagger = A$, then A is called *self-adjoint* or *Hermitian*.[9]

For example, consider the operator Q. Let the domain of Q be the set of all vectors ψ such that $x\psi(x)$ is square integrable. This is dense. For any vector ψ let the sequence of vectors ψ_n be defined by $\psi_n(x) = \psi(x)$ for $-n \leq x \leq n$ and $\psi_n(x) = 0$ for $|x| > n$. Then $x\psi_n(x)$ is square integrable, so ψ_n is in the domain of Q for each n, and

$$\|\psi - \psi_n\|^2 = \int_{-\infty}^{-n} |\psi(x)|^2\,dx + \int_n^\infty |\psi(x)|^2\,dx \to 0$$

as $n \to \infty$, so $\psi_n \to \psi$. The first equation of this section shows that Q is symmetric. Therefore $Q^\dagger$ is an extension of Q.

Is Q self-adjoint or is the domain of $Q^\dagger$ larger than the domain of Q? Let ψ be a vector in the domain of $Q^\dagger$. This means there is a vector $\chi = Q^\dagger\psi$ such that $(\phi, \chi) = (Q\phi, \psi)$ or

$$\int_{-\infty}^\infty \phi(x)^*\chi(x)\,dx = \int_{-\infty}^\infty \phi(x)^*x\psi(x)\,dx$$

for all vectors ϕ in the domain of Q. For each positive integer n this holds for all vectors ϕ such that $\phi(x) = 0$ for $|x| > n$. Let $\chi_n(x) = \chi(x)$ for $-n \leq x \leq n$ and $\chi_n(x) = 0$ for $|x| > n$, and let $\psi_n(x) = \psi(x)$ for $-n \leq x \leq n$ and $\psi_n(x) = 0$ for $|x| > n$. By considering these as vectors in $L^2(-n, n)$, we conclude that $\chi_n(x) = x\psi_n(x)$. It follows that $\chi(x) = x\psi(x)$. This implies that $x\psi(x)$ is square integrable, which means that ψ is in the domain of Q. Therefore the domain of $Q^\dagger$ is not larger than the domain of Q. Thus $Q^\dagger = Q$, so Q is self-adjoint.

Evidently a symmetric operator A can fail to be self-adjoint only if $A^\dagger$ is an extension of A to a larger domain. If a symmetric operator cannot be extended to a symmetric operator on a larger domain, we call it a *maximal symmetric* operator.

Theorem 11.2. Every self-adjoint operator is a maximal symmetric operator.

Proof. Let A be a self-adjoint operator and let B be a symmetric operator that is an extension of A. From the definition of the adjoint we can see that $A^\dagger$ is an extension of $B^\dagger$. But $B^\dagger$ is an extension of B, because B is symmetric. Therefore $A^\dagger$ is an extension of B. Thus A is an extension of B, because $A = A^\dagger$. This implies that $A = B$ and completes the proof.

[9] In mathematics the word Hermitian could be used for symmetric, but in common physics usage Hermitian means self-adjoint.

Thus, to be self-adjoint, it is necessary that a symmetric operator be extended to a maximal symmetric operator. But this is not sufficient; there are maximal symmetric operators which are not self-adjoint.[10]

Unbounded operators are not continuous; we have to settle for the next best thing.

Definition.   An operator A is *closed* if whenever a sequence of vectors ψ_n in the domain of A converges to a limit vector ψ and the sequence of vectors $A\psi_n$ converges to a limit vector ϕ, then ψ is in the domain of A and $A\psi = \phi$.

Consider an infinite linear combination $\psi = \sum_{k=1}^{\infty} x_k\phi_k$ where all the vectors ϕ_k are in the domain of A. Then each partial sum $\psi_n = \sum_{k=1}^{n} x_k\phi_k$ is in the domain of A and

$$A\psi_n = \sum_{k=1}^{n} x_k A\phi_k.$$

The sequence of vectors ψ_n converges to ψ. Suppose the sequence of vectors $A\psi_n$ converges to a limit vector

$$\phi = \sum_{k=1}^{\infty} x_k A\phi_k.$$

If A is closed, then $\sum_{k=1}^{\infty} x_k\phi_k$ is in the domain of A and

$$A\sum_{k=1}^{\infty} x_k\phi_k = \sum_{k=1}^{\infty} x_k A\phi_k.$$

Theorem 11.3.   Let A be an operator with a dense domain. Its adjoint $A^\dagger$ is closed.

Proof.   Suppose a sequence of vectors ψ_n in the domain of $A^\dagger$ converges to a limit vector ψ and the sequence of vectors $A^\dagger\psi_n$ converges to a limit vector χ. Then for every vector ϕ in the domain of A

$$(\phi, \chi) = (A\phi, \psi),$$

because

$$(\phi, A^\dagger\psi_n) = (A\phi, \psi_n)$$

$$(\phi, A^\dagger\psi_n) \to (\phi, \chi)$$

and

$$(A\phi, \psi_n) \to (A\phi, \psi).$$

[10] An example is the operator A defined by $(A\psi)(x) = i(d/dx)\,\psi(x)$ on $L^2(0, \infty)$. For A to be symmetric its domain must be restricted to vectors ψ such that $\psi(0) = 0$, but the domain of $A^\dagger$ is not so restricted. See Stone, Theorem 10.8.

It follows that ψ is in the domain of $A^\dagger$ and $A^\dagger\psi = \chi$. This completes the proof.

Thus every self-adjoint operator is closed.

Unbounded self-adjoint operators play important roles in some of the following discussions; however, questions of domains generally are suppressed.

See *Exercises and Applications* 1, 3, and 4.

3

DIAGONALIZING OPERATORS

To use linear operators in quantum mechanics we should know how to diagonalize them. We will see that putting operators in diagonal form makes working with them almost as easy as working with numbers. Some things work out better for complex vector spaces than for real vector spaces. From now on we consider operators defined on a complex separable Hilbert space.

12. EIGENVALUES AND EIGENVECTORS

Let B be a linear operator. If ψ is a nonzero vector and b is a scalar such that $B\psi = b\psi$, then we say that ψ is an *eigenvector* of B and b is an *eigenvalue* of B. What is required for a number to be an eigenvalue of a linear operator?

Theorem 12.1. If b is an eigenvalue of a linear operator B, then the operator $B - b$ has no inverse.

Proof. If $B - b$ has an inverse, then there is no nonzero vector ϕ such that $(B - b)\phi = 0$.[1]
For a finite-dimensional space this is all that is required.

Theorem 12.2. If B is a linear operator on a finite-dimensional space, then each of the following is a necessary and sufficient condition for a scalar b to be an eigenvalue of B.

(i) The operator $B - b$ has no inverse.
(ii) The determinant of the matrix corresponding to $B - b$ is zero.

[1] See Section 7, *Inverses.*

Proof.   The operator $B - b$ has an inverse if and only if there is no non-zero vector ϕ such that $(B - b)\phi = 0$ (Theorem 7.2). Also $B - b$ has an inverse if and only if the determinant of the matrix corresponding to $B - b$ is not zero (Theorem 7.2).

Condition (ii) gives us a way to calculate eigenvalues. If the space is n-dimensional, we get an $n \times n$ matrix for $B - b$. Setting the determinant of this matrix equal to zero gives us an nth-order polynomial equation to solve for b. Such equations always have at least one solution and never have more than n distinct solutions. Thus a linear operator on an n-dimensional space has at least one eigenvalue and at most n distinct eigenvalues.[2] It does not matter which basis is used to set up the matrix corresponding to $B - b$. The eigenvalues calculated from condition (ii) can not depend on the basis, because the theorem holds for any basis.

That eigenvalues calculated from a matrix are independent of the basis reflects the following fact, which also is valid for an infinite-dimensional space.

Theorem 12.3.   If T is a linear operator which has an inverse T^{-1}, then operators B and TBT^{-1} have the same eigenvalues.

Proof.   Let b be an eigenvalue of B. This means there is a nonzero vector ψ such that $B\psi = b\psi$. If T has an inverse T^{-1}, then $T\psi$ is not zero and

$$TBT^{-1}T\psi = TB\psi = Tb\psi = bT\psi,$$

so b is an eigenvalue of TBT^{-1}. That every eigenvalue of TBT^{-1} is an eigenvalue of B is proved similarly using $B = T^{-1}TBT^{-1}T$.

Our main interest is in Hermitian and unitary operators. The most important properties of their eigenvalues and eigenvectors are the following.

Theorem 12.4.   Every eigenvalue of a Hermitian operator is a real number.

Proof.   If A is Hermitian and a is an eigenvalue of A with eigenvector ψ, then

$$a(\psi, \psi) = (\psi, A\psi) = (A\psi, \psi) = (a\psi, \psi) = a^*(\psi, \psi),$$

which implies that $a = a^*$ because ψ is not zero.

Theorem 12.5.   Every eigenvalue of a unitary operator is a complex number of absolute value one.

---

[2] Complex scalars are needed to get a solution for every polynomial equation. On a real finite-dimensional space there are operators which have no eigenvalues.

Proof. If U is a unitary operator and u is an eigenvalue of U with eigenvector ψ, then

$$(\psi, \psi) = (U\psi, U\psi) = (u\psi, u\psi) = u^*u(\psi, \psi),$$

which implies that $|u|^2 = 1$ because ψ is not zero.

Theorem 12.6. Two eigenvectors of a Hermitian or unitary operator are orthogonal if they correspond to different eigenvalues.

Proof. If A is Hermitian and ψ_1 and ψ_2 are eigenvectors of A corresponding to eigenvalues a_1 and a_2, then

$$(a_1 - a_2)(\psi_1, \psi_2) = (a_1\psi_1, \psi_2) - (\psi_1, a_2\psi_2) = (A\psi_1, \psi_2) - (\psi_1, A\psi_2) = 0,$$

which implies that $(\psi_1, \psi_2) = 0$ when $a_1 \neq a_2$. If U is unitary and ψ_1 and ψ_2 are eigenvectors of U corresponding to eigenvalues u_1 and u_2, then

$$u_1^*u_2(\psi_1, \psi_2) = (u_1\psi_1, u_2\psi_2) = (U\psi_1, U\psi_2) = (\psi_1, \psi_2),$$

which implies that $(\psi_1, \psi_2) = 0$ when $u_1^*u_2 \neq 1$. If $u_1 \neq u_2$, then $u_1^*u_2 \neq 1$ because if $u_1^*u_2 = 1$, then $u_1 = u_1u_1^*u_2 = u_2$. This completes the proof of the theorem.

The first two theorems strengthen the analogies of Hermitian operators to real numbers and unitary operators to complex numbers of absolute value one.

Let b be an eigenvalue of a linear operator B and let $\mathcal{M}_b$ be the set of all vectors ψ such that $B\psi = b\psi$. Evidently $\mathcal{M}_b$ is a linear manifold; if ψ and ϕ are in $\mathcal{M}_b$ and c is a scalar, then

$$B(\psi + \phi) = B\psi + B\phi = b\psi + b\phi = b(\psi + \phi)$$

and

$$Bc\psi = cB\psi = cb\psi = bc\psi,$$

so $\psi + \phi$ and $c\psi$ are in $\mathcal{M}_b$. If B is bounded or if B is unbounded but closed, then $\mathcal{M}_b$ is a subspace; if a sequence of vectors ψ_n in $\mathcal{M}_b$ converges to a limit vector ψ, then the sequence of vectors $B\psi_n = b\psi_n$ converges to the limit vector $b\psi$ so $B\psi = b\psi$ and ψ is in $\mathcal{M}_b$. On this subspace B acts like the scalar multiple b of the identity operator; it just multiplies every vector in $\mathcal{M}_b$ by b.

For a Hermitian or unitary operator the eigenvector subspaces corresponding to different eigenvalues are mutually orthogonal, and the operator acts on them like a diagonal matrix, constructed as follows. Let A be Hermitian or unitary and let $a_1, a_2, \ldots, a_k, \ldots$ be its different eigenvalues. For each k let $\mathcal{M}_k$ be the eigenvector subspace for a_k and let the set of vectors

$\phi_1{}^k, \phi_2{}^k, \ldots, \phi_s{}^k, \ldots$ be an orthonormal basis for $\mathcal{M}_k$.[3] Since eigenvectors for different eigenvalues are orthogonal, the set of all vectors $\phi_s{}^k$ for different k is orthonormal: $(\phi_r{}^j, \phi_s{}^k) = \delta_{jk}\delta_{rs}$. Consider the subspace $\mathcal{M} = \sum_k \oplus \mathcal{M}_k$ of all linear combinations $\sum_{k,s} x_s{}^k\phi_s{}^k$. We refer to this as the subspace spanned by the eigenvectors of A. Evidently the set of vectors $\phi_s{}^k$ is an orthonormal basis for $\mathcal{M}$. We have $A\phi_s{}^k = a_k\phi_s{}^k$ and $(\phi_r{}^j, A\phi_s{}^k) = a_k\delta_{jk}\delta_{rs}$. On this subspace A acts like a diagonal matrix. Its off-diagonal matrix elements are zero. Its diagonal matrix elements are eigenvalues. For any vector $\psi = \sum_{k,s} x_s{}^k\phi_s{}^k$ in $\mathcal{M}$ we have $A\psi = \sum_{k,s} a_k x_s{}^k\phi_s{}^k$.

We say that a subspace $\mathcal{M}$ *reduces* a linear operator A if $A\psi$ is in $\mathcal{M}$ for every vector ψ in $\mathcal{M}$ and $A\phi$ is in $\mathcal{M}^\perp$ for every vector ϕ in $\mathcal{M}^\perp$.[4,5] Let E be the projection operator onto $\mathcal{M}$.

Theorem 12.7. The following statements are equivalent:

(i) $\mathcal{M}$ reduces A;
(ii) $EA = AE$;
(iii) $(1 - E)A = A(1 - E)$.

Proof. That (ii) and (iii) are equivalent is obvious. We show that (i) implies (ii) and that (ii) and (iii) imply (i). For any vector[5] $\psi = \psi_\mathcal{M} + \psi_{\mathcal{M}^\perp}$ we have $A\psi = A\psi_\mathcal{M} + A\psi_{\mathcal{M}^\perp}$. If $\mathcal{M}$ reduces A, then $A\psi_\mathcal{M}$ is in $\mathcal{M}$ and $A\psi_{\mathcal{M}^\perp}$ is in $\mathcal{M}^\perp$. Therefore $EA\psi = A\psi_\mathcal{M} = AE\psi$. Thus (i) implies (ii). If ψ is in $\mathcal{M}$ and $EA = AE$, then $E\psi = \psi$ and $A\psi = AE\psi = EA\psi$ so $A\psi$ is in $\mathcal{M}$. If ϕ is in $\mathcal{M}^\perp$ and $(1 - E)A = A(1 - E)$, then $(1 - E)\phi = \phi$ and $A\phi = A(1 - E)\phi = (1 - E)A\phi$ so $A\phi$ is in $\mathcal{M}^\perp$. Thus (ii) and (iii) imply (i). This completes the proof.

If $\mathcal{M}$ reduces A, then $A = AE + A(1 - E)$ is a sum of two completely separate parts; we may think of AE as an operator on $\mathcal{M}$ and of $A(1 - E)$ as an operator on $\mathcal{M}^\perp$.

Theorem 12.8. Let A be a Hermitian operator and let $\mathcal{M}$ be the subspace spanned by the eigenvectors of A. Then $\mathcal{M}$ reduces A.[6]

---

[3] The number of eigenvalues a_k may be finite or infinite. It is always countable; if there were an uncountable number of different eigenvalues, then there would be an uncountable number of orthonormal eigenvectors, which is impossible in a separable Hilbert space. The dimension of $\mathcal{M}_k$, which is the number of basis vectors $\phi_s{}^k$ in $\mathcal{M}_k$ or the range of the index s, also may be finite or infinite and may be different for different values of k.

[4] For an unbounded operator this definition and the following theorem have to be stated more carefully to take account of domains. See Riesz and Nagy, Section 116.

[5] See Section 3, *Hilbert Space*.

[6] This holds for an unbounded Hermitian operator provided "reduces" is properly defined; see footnote 4.

Proof. That $A\psi$ is in $\mathcal{M}$ if ψ is in $\mathcal{M}$ is clear from the previous discussion. If ϕ is in $\mathcal{M}^\perp$, then $(\psi, A\phi) = (A\psi, \phi)$ is zero for any vector ψ in $\mathcal{M}$, so $A\phi$ is in $\mathcal{M}^\perp$.

Theorem 12.9. Let U be a unitary operator and let $\mathcal{M}$ be the subspace spanned by the eigenvectors of U. Then $\mathcal{M}$ reduces U.

Proof. Let ϕ be in $\mathcal{M}^\perp$. If ψ is an eigenvector of U with eigenvalue u, $U\psi = u\psi$, then

$$u^*(\psi, U\phi) = (U\psi, U\phi) = (\psi, \phi) = 0,$$

which implies that $(\psi, U\phi) = 0$, because $|u| = 1$. In particular $U\phi$ is orthogonal to every vector of an orthonormal basis for $\mathcal{M}$, because $\mathcal{M}$ has an orthonormal basis of eigenvectors. Therefore $U\phi$ is in $\mathcal{M}^\perp$. This completes the proof.

Thus a Hermitian or unitary operator splits into two completely separate parts. One part is an operator on the subspace spanned by the eigenvectors. It can be represented by a diagonal matrix of eigenvalues, with respect to an orthonormal basis of eigenvectors. The other part is an operator on the orthogonal complement of the subspace spanned by the eigenvectors.

The simplest possibility is that the eigenvectors of an operator span the whole space. Then there is an orthonormal basis of eigenvectors for the whole space, and the operator corresponds to a diagonal matrix with respect to this basis. Its eigenvalues are the diagonal matrix elements. For example, this is always the case for projection operators. Let E be the projection operator onto a subspace $\mathcal{N}$. If there is a nonzero vector ψ such that $E\psi = a\psi$, then

$$a^2\psi = aE\psi = E^2\psi = E\psi = a\psi,$$

so either $a = 1$ or $a = 0$. A projection operator can have only two different eigenvalues: one and zero. If ψ is in $\mathcal{N}$, then $E\psi = \psi$. If ψ is in $\mathcal{N}^\perp$, then $E\psi = 0$. Thus $\mathcal{N}$ is the eigenvector subspace for the eigenvalue one, and $\mathcal{N}^\perp$ is the eigenvector subspace for the eigenvalue zero. By combining an orthonormal basis for $\mathcal{N}$ and an orthonormal basis for $\mathcal{N}^\perp$ we get an orthonormal basis of eigenvectors of E for the whole space. The off-diagonal matrix elements of E for this basis all are zero. The diagonal matrix elements of E are one for basis vectors from $\mathcal{N}$ and zero for basis vectors from $\mathcal{N}^\perp$. Thus a projection operator can be described completely in terms of its eigenvalues and eigenvectors.

13. EIGENVALUE DECOMPOSITION

For a finite-dimensional space every Hermitian or unitary operator can be described completely in terms of its eigenvalues and eigenvectors.

Theorem 13.1. For a finite-dimensional space the eigenvectors of a Hermitian or unitary operator span the whole space.[7]

Proof. Let A be a Hermitian or unitary operator on a finite-dimensional space, let $\mathcal{M}$ be the subspace spanned by its eigenvectors, and let E be the projection operator onto $\mathcal{M}$. We know (Theorems 12.8 and 12.9) that $\mathcal{M}$ reduces A. Suppose $\mathcal{M}$ is not the whole space. Consider $A(1 - E)$ as an operator on $\mathcal{M}^\perp$. Since every operator on a finite-dimensional space has at least one eigenvalue, there must be a number a and nonzero vector ϕ in $\mathcal{M}^\perp$ such that $A(1 - E)\phi = a\phi$. Then

$$A\phi = AE\phi + A(1 - E)\phi = A(1 - E)\phi = a\phi,$$

so ϕ is an eigenvector of A. This contradicts the assumption that $\mathcal{M}$ is not the whole space and completes the proof.

This means that for each Hermitian or unitary operator A on a finite-dimensional space there is an orthonormal basis of eigenvectors. Let $a_1, a_2, \ldots, a_m$ be the different eigenvalues of A. For each $k = 1, 2, \ldots, m$ let $\mathcal{M}_k$ be the eigenvector subspace for a_k and let $\phi_s{}^k$ be orthonormal basis vectors for $\mathcal{M}_k$. Thus $A\phi_s{}^k = a_k\phi_s{}^k$. The set of all vectors $\phi_s{}^k$ is an orthonormal basis for the whole space. If the space is n-dimensional, the total number of vectors $\phi_s{}^k$ is n, and $m \leq n$. The number of orthonormal eigenvectors $\phi_s{}^k$ for an eigenvalue a_k may be different for different values of k. If A has n different eigenvalues, then $m = n$ and there is only one vector $\phi_s{}^k$ for each k; the index s is unnecessary for this case.

The matrix elements of A with respect to this basis are $(\phi_r{}^j, A\phi_s{}^k) = a_k\delta_{jk}\delta_{rs}$. The off-diagonal matrix elements are zero and the diagonal matrix elements are eigenvalues. Any vector ψ is a linear combination $\psi = \sum_{k,s} x_s{}^k\phi_s{}^k$; we have $A\psi = \sum_{k,s} a_k x_s{}^k\phi_s{}^k$. Thus, when a Hermitian or unitary operator on a finite-dimensional space is expressed in terms of its eigenvalues and eigenvectors, it corresponds simply to a diagonal matrix.

[7] For a real finite-dimensional space this is true for a Hermitian operator, but not for a unitary operator. The proof for a Hermitian operator is necessarily quite different; see Birkhoff and MacLane, Chapter IX, Section 10. A unitary operator which has no real eigenvalues is defined by the 2×2 matrix $u_{11} = 0 = u_{22}$ and $u_{12} = 1 = -u_{21}$.

There is a more economical way to state this. For each $k = 1, 2, \ldots, m$ let I_k be the projection operator onto $\mathcal{M}_k$. Then

$$A = \sum_{k=1}^{m} a_k I_k.$$

These projection operators are mutually orthogonal; $I_j I_k = \delta_{jk} I_k$. They have the completeness property that $\sum_{k=1}^{m} I_k = 1$. In Dirac notation we write $|a_k, s\rangle$ for $\phi_s{}^k$. Then

$$I_k = \sum_s |a_k, s\rangle\langle a_k, s|$$

and

$$A = \sum_k a_k \sum_s |a_k, s\rangle\langle a_k, s|.$$

Finally, we express this in a way which is less economical for a finite-dimensional space but is suitable also for any Hermitian or unitary operator on an infinite-dimensional space. First, consider a Hermitian operator A. Label its eigenvalues in the order

$$a_1 < a_2 < \cdots < a_{m-1} < a_m.$$

For each real number x let

$$E_x = \sum_{a_k \leq x} I_k.$$

This is the projection operator onto the subspace spanned by all eigenvectors for eigenvalues $a_k \leq x$. Evidently E_x is zero for $x < a_1$. If $x \geq a_m$, then $E_x = 1$, because $\sum_{k=1}^{m} I_k = 1$. The orthogonality property $I_j I_k = \delta_{jk} I_k$ implies that if $x \leq y$, then

$$E_x E_y = E_x = E^y E_x$$

or $E_x \leq E_y$. Thus E_x increases from zero to one as x increases through the spectrum of eigenvalues; E_x increases by I_k when x reaches the eigenvalue a_k. For each x let

$$dE_x = E_x - E_{x-\epsilon}$$

with ϵ positive but small enough that there is no eigenvalue a_j such that $x - \epsilon \leq a_j < x$. Then dE_x is not zero only when x is an eigenvalue a_k and $dE_x = I_k$ for $x = a_k$. For $\sum_{k=1}^{m} I_k = 1$ we can write

$$\int_{-\infty}^{\infty} dE_x = 1,$$

and for $A = \sum_{k=1}^{m} a_k I_k$ we can write

$$A = \int_{-\infty}^{\infty} x \, dE_x.$$

For any vectors ψ and ϕ we have[8]

$$(\phi, \psi) = \int_{-\infty}^{\infty} d(\phi, E_x \psi)$$

and

$$(\phi, A\psi) = \int_{-\infty}^{\infty} x \, d(\phi, E_x \psi),$$

in which $(\phi, E_x \psi)$ is a complex function of x which jumps in value by $(\phi, I_k \psi)$ at $x = a_k$.

Unitary operators can be treated similarly. For a unitary operator U let the eigenvalues be $u_k = e^{i\theta_k}$, labeled in the order

$$0 < \theta_1 < \theta_2 < \cdots < \theta_{m-1} < \theta_m \leq 2\pi.$$

For each real number x let

$$E_x = \sum_{\theta_k \leq x} I_k.$$

This is the projection operator onto the subspace spanned by all eigenvectors for eigenvalues $e^{i\theta_k}$ with $\theta_k \leq x$. If $x \leq 0$, then $E_x = 0$. If $x \geq 2\pi$, then $E_x = 1$. Evidently E_x increases by increments I_k the same as for a Hermitian operator with eigenvalues θ_k. For

$$U = \sum_{k=1}^{m} u_k I_k = \sum_{k=1}^{m} e^{i\theta_k} I_k$$

we can write

$$U = \int_0^{2\pi} e^{ix} \, dE_x.$$

For any vectors ψ and ϕ we have[8]

$$(\phi, U\psi) = \int_0^{2\pi} e^{ix} \, d(\phi, E_x \psi).$$

We have defined the operators E_x so that they are continuous from the right as a function of x in the sense that if ϵ is positive, then $E_{x+\epsilon}\psi \to E_x\psi$ as $\epsilon \to 0$ for any vector ψ and any x. From the left E_x has discontinuities $dE_x = I_k$ at $x = a_k$ or θ_k.

---

[8] These are ordinary Riemann-Stieltjes integrals: $\int_a^b g(x) \, dF(x)$ is the limit of

$$\sum_{k=1}^{n} g(x_k)[F(x_k) - F(x_{k-1})]$$

as $n \to \infty$ and $a < x_0 < x_1 < x_2 \cdots < x_n \leq b$ divides the range of integration into smaller and smaller pieces; see Riesz and Nagy, Section 49.

14. SPECTRAL DECOMPOSITION

On an infinite-dimensional space there are Hermitian and unitary operators which have no eigenvalues or eigenvectors, but the decomposition into projection operators still is applicable in the integral form we have just developed.

Definition. A family of projection operators E_x depending on a real parameter x is a *spectral family* if it has the following properties:

(i) If $x \leq y$, then $E_x \leq E_y$ or $E_x E_y = E_x = E_y E_x$;
(ii) If ϵ is positive, then $E_{x+\epsilon}\psi \to E_x\psi$ as $\epsilon \to 0$ for any vector ψ and any x;
(iii) $E_x\psi \to 0$ as $x \to -\infty$ and $E_x\psi \to \psi$ as $x \to +\infty$ for any vector ψ.

Theorem 14.1. For each self-adjoint operator A there is a unique spectral family of projection operators E_x such that[8]

$$(\phi, A\psi) = \int_{-\infty}^{\infty} x \, d(\phi, E_x\psi)$$

for all vectors ψ and ϕ.[9]

We write[10]

$$A = \int_{-\infty}^{\infty} x \, dE_x.$$

This is called the *spectral decomposition* or *spectral resolution* of A. Unitary operators have similar spectral decompositions.

Theorem 14.2. For each unitary operator U there is a unique spectral family of projection operators E_x such that $E_x = 0$ for $x \leq 0$ and $E_x = 1$ for $x \geq 2\pi$ and[8]

$$(\phi, U\psi) = \int_0^{2\pi} e^{ix} \, d(\phi, E_x\psi)$$

for all vectors ψ and ϕ.[11]

We write[12]

$$U = \int_0^{2\pi} e^{ix} \, dE_x.$$

This is called the *spectral decomposition* or *spectral resolution* of U.

---

[9] For an unbounded self-adjoint operator A this equation is restricted to vectors ψ in the domain of A. For a proof of the theorem see Stone, Theorem 5.9.
[10] This can be established as an operator integral; see Riesz and Nagy, Sections 107 and 120.
[11] See Stone, Theorem 8.4.
[12] This can be established as an operator integral; see Riesz and Nagy, Section 109.

For example, consider the space $L^2(0, 1)$ of complex square-integrable functions $\psi(x)$ for $0 \leq x \leq 1$. Let A be the self-adjoint operator defined by $(A\psi)(x) = x\psi(x)$ for every vector ψ. Let E_x be the projection operators defined by $(E_x\psi)(y) = \psi(y)$ if $y \leq x$ and $(E_x\psi)(y) = 0$ if $y > x$. For any vectors ψ and ϕ

$$\int_{-\infty}^{\infty} x\, d(\phi, E_x\psi) = \int_{-\infty}^{\infty} x\, d \int_0^1 \phi(y)^*(E_x\psi)(y)\, dy$$

$$= \int_0^1 x\, d \int_0^x \phi(y)^*\, \psi(y)\, dy = \int_0^1 \phi(x)^*\, x\psi(x)\, dx$$

$$= (\phi, A\psi).$$

It is obvious that if $x \leq y$, then $E_x \leq E_y$. For ϵ positive

$$\|E_{x+\epsilon}\psi - E_x\psi\|^2 = \int_x^{x+\epsilon} |\psi(y)|^2\, dy \to 0$$

as $\epsilon \to 0$ for any vector ψ and x in the interval $0 \leq x < 1$. Evidently $E_x = 0$ if $x < 0$ and $E_x = 1$ if $x \geq 1$. Thus the family of projection operators E_x is a spectral family, and we have the spectral decomposition of A. Note that $E_x\psi$ is continuous from the left as well as from the right as a function of x. In particular for any vectors ψ and ϕ

$$(\phi, E_x\psi) - (\phi, E_{x-\epsilon}\psi) = \int_{x-\epsilon}^x \phi(y)^*\, \psi(y)\, dy \to 0$$

as $\epsilon \to 0$, so $(\phi, E_x\psi)$ never jumps in value; it is a continuous function of x.

The operator Q defined by $(Q\psi)(x) = x\psi(x)$ on $L^2(-\infty, \infty)$ also has the spectral decomposition

$$Q = \int_{-\infty}^{\infty} x\, dE_x$$

with E_x defined by $(E_x\psi)(y) = \psi(y)$ if $y \leq x$ and $(E_x\psi)(y) = 0$ if $y > x$ for any vector ψ. The only difference between this spectral family and that of the previous example is that here E_x increases over the whole range $-\infty < x < \infty$ with $E_x = 0$ being reached only as $x \to -\infty$ and $E_x = 1$ as $x \to +\infty$.

For an example of the spectral decomposition of a unitary operator consider again the space $L^2(0, 1)$ and let U be the unitary operator defined by $(U\psi)(x) = e^{i2\pi x}\psi(x)$ for every vector ψ. Let $(E_x\psi)(y) = \psi(y)$ if $y \leq x/2\pi$ and $(E_x\psi)(y) = 0$ if $y > x/2\pi$. This defines a spectral family of projection operators E_x. Evidently $E_x = 0$ if $x \leq 0$ and $E_x = 1$ if $x \geq 2\pi$. For any vectors ψ and ϕ

$$\int_0^{2\pi} e^{ix}\, d(\phi, E_x\psi) = \int_0^{2\pi} e^{ix}\, d\int_0^{x/2\pi} \phi(y)^*\, \psi(y)\, dy = \int_0^{2\pi} e^{ix}\phi\left(\frac{x}{2\pi}\right)^*\psi\left(\frac{x}{2\pi}\right)\frac{dx}{2\pi}$$

$$= \int_0^1 \phi(y)^* e^{i2\pi y}\, \psi(y)\, dy = (\phi, U\psi).$$

Thus we have the spectral decomposition of U.

These examples illustrate the main new feature which makes the infinite-dimensional case different from the finite-dimensional: E_x may increase continuously as a function of x instead of by discrete jumps. We say that E_x *jumps* in value at x if there is a vector ψ such that for ϵ positive $(E_x - E_{x-\epsilon})\psi$ does not converge to zero as $\epsilon \to 0$. Otherwise we say that E_x is *continuous* at x. In each of the examples just cited E_x is continuous for all x. There are no jumps. This is because we considered operators A, Q, and U which have no eigenvalues or eigenvectors.

Theorem 14.3. Let A be a self-adjoint operator with the spectral decomposition

$$A = \int_{-\infty}^{\infty} x\, dE_x.$$

Then E_x jumps in value at $x = a$ if and only if a is an eigenvalue of A. Let I_a be the projection operator onto the subspace spanned by the eigenvectors of A for the eigenvalue a. Then $E_x I_a = 0$ for $x < a$ and $E_x I_a = I_a$ for $x \geq a$, and for ϵ positive

$$E_a\psi - E_{a-\epsilon}\psi \to I_a\psi$$

as $\epsilon \to 0$ for any vector ψ.

Proof. For $\epsilon > \delta > 0$ and any vector ψ

$$\|(E_a - E_{a-\epsilon})\psi - (E_a - E_{a-\delta})\psi\|^2 = \|(E_a - E_{a-\epsilon})\psi\|^2 + \|(E_a - E_{a-\delta})\psi\|^2$$
$$-\big(\psi, (E_a - E_{a-\epsilon})(E_a - E_{a-\delta})\psi\big) - \big(\psi, (E_a - E_{a-\delta})(E_a - E_{a-\epsilon})\psi\big)$$
$$= \|(E_a - E_{a-\epsilon})\psi\|^2 - \|(E_a - E_{a-\delta})\psi\|^2$$

because $E_a - E_{a-\epsilon}$ and $E_a - E_{a-\delta}$ are projection operators and $E_a - E_{a-\epsilon} \geq E_a - E_{a-\delta}$. This equation shows that $\|(E_a - E_{a-\epsilon})\psi\|^2$ is monotonically decreasing as $\epsilon \to 0$. This implies that $\|(E_a - E_{a-\epsilon})\psi\|^2$ converges to a limit as $\epsilon \to 0$, which implies that

$$\|(E_a - E_{a-\epsilon})\psi\|^2 - \|(E_a - E_{a-\delta})\psi\|^2 \to 0$$

as ϵ, $\delta \to 0$. Thus the first equation shows that the vectors $(E_a - E_{a-\epsilon})\psi$ have the Cauchy property as $\epsilon \to 0$. Because the space is complete,

$(E_a - E_{a-\epsilon})\psi$ must converge to a limit vector as $\epsilon \to 0$. Call this limit vector ψ_a.

Suppose ψ_a is not zero. If $x \geq a$, then

$$E_x(E_a - E_{a-\epsilon}) = E_x E_a - E_x E_{a-\epsilon} = E_a - E_{a-\epsilon}.$$

If $x < a$, then for ϵ small enough that $x < a - \epsilon$

$$E_x(E_a - E_{a-\epsilon}) = E_x E_a - E_x E_{a-\epsilon} = E_x - E_x = 0.$$

Therefore $E_x\psi_a = 0$ for $x < a$ and $E_x\psi_a = \psi_a$ for $x \geq a$, so

$$(\phi, A\psi_a) = \int_{-\infty}^{\infty} x \, d(\phi, E_x\psi_a) = a(\phi, \psi_a) = (\phi, a\psi_a)$$

for any vector ϕ, which means that $A\psi_a = a\psi_a$. Thus a is an eigenvalue and ψ_a is an eigenvector.

For any vectors ψ and ϕ we have

$$(\phi, A^2\psi) = \int_{-\infty}^{\infty} x \, d(\phi, E_x A\psi) = \int_{-\infty}^{\infty} x \, d(E_x\phi, A\psi)$$

$$= \int_{-\infty}^{\infty} x \, d_x \int_{-\infty}^{\infty} y \, d_y(E_x\phi, E_y\psi) = \int_{-\infty}^{\infty} x \, d_x \int_{-\infty}^{\infty} y \, d_y(\phi, E_x E_y\psi)$$

$$= \int_{-\infty}^{\infty} x \, d_x \int_{-\infty}^{x} y \, d_y(\phi, E_y\psi) = \int_{-\infty}^{\infty} x^2 \, d(\phi, E_x\psi),$$

because $E_x E_y = E_y$ for $y \leq x$, and for $y > x$

$$(\phi, E_x E_y\psi) = (\phi, E_x\psi),$$

which is independent of y.

Suppose a is an eigenvalue of A and let I_a be the projection onto the subspace of eigenvectors. Then

$$\int_{-\infty}^{\infty} (x^2 - 2ax + a^2) \, d(\phi, E_x I_a\psi) = (\phi, [A^2 - 2aA + a^2]I_a\psi) = 0$$

for any vectors ψ and ϕ. For $\phi = I_a\psi$ we have

$$(\phi, E_x I_a\psi) = (I_a\psi, E_x^2 I_a\psi) = \|E_x I_a\psi\|^2$$

and

$$\int_{-\infty}^{\infty} (x - a)^2 \, d\|E_x I_a\psi\|^2 = 0.$$

Because $\|E_x I_a\psi\|^2$ is a monotonically increasing function of x,[13] we see that it can change in value only at $x = a$. But $\|E_x I_a\psi\|^2 \to 0$ as $x \to -\infty$ and

[13] See Section 10, *Projection Operators*.

$\|E_x I_a \psi\|^2 \rightarrow \|I_a \psi\|^2$ as $x \rightarrow +\infty$. Therefore $\|E_x I_a \psi\|^2 = 0$ if $x < a$, and $\|E_x I_a \psi\|^2 = \|I_a \psi\|^2$ if $x \geq a$ for any vector ψ. This implies that $E_x I_a = 0$ for $x < a$ and $E_x I_a = I_a$ for $x \geq a$. For any vector ψ we have

$$(E_a - E_{a-\epsilon}) I_a \psi = (E_a I_a - E_{a-\epsilon} I_a) \psi = I_a \psi.$$

Thus E_x jumps in value at $x = a$.

For any vector ψ

$$\|(E_a - E_{a-\epsilon})(1 - I_a) \psi\|^2 = ([1 - I_a]\psi, [E_a - E_{a-\epsilon}]^2 [1 - I_a]\psi)$$
$$= ([1 - I_a]\psi, [E_a - E_{a-\epsilon}][1 - I_a]\psi) \rightarrow 0$$

as $\epsilon \rightarrow 0$, because $[E_a - E_{a-\epsilon}][1 - I_a]\psi$ converges to a limit and if this limit were not zero, it would be an eigenvector which is orthogonal to $[1 - I_a]\psi$. Thus for any vector ψ

$$(E_a - E_{a-\epsilon}) \psi = (E_a - E_{a-\epsilon}) I_a \psi + (E_a - E_{a-\epsilon})(1 - I_a) \psi$$
$$= I_a \psi + (E_a - E_{a-\epsilon})(1 - I_a) \psi \rightarrow I_a \psi$$

as $\epsilon \rightarrow 0$. This completes the proof of the theorem.

The similar statement for unitary operators is the following.

Theorem 14.4. Let U be a unitary operator with the spectral decomposition

$$U = \int_0^{2\pi} e^{ix} \, dE_x.$$

Then E_x jumps in value at $x = \theta$ if and only if $e^{i\theta}$ is an eigenvalue of U. Let I_θ be the projection operator onto the subspace spanned by the eigenvectors of U for the eigenvalue $e^{i\theta}$. Then $E_x I_\theta = 0$ for $x < \theta$ and $E_x I_\theta = I_\theta$ for $x \geq \theta$, and for ϵ positive

$$E_\theta \psi - E_{\theta-\epsilon} \psi \rightarrow I_\theta \psi$$

as $\epsilon \rightarrow 0$ for any vector ψ.

Proof. The proof is almost identical to that of the preceding theorem. That $\|E_x I_\theta \psi\|^2$ can change its value only at $x = \theta$ is shown by

$$\int_0^{2\pi} |e^{ix} - e^{i\theta}|^2 \, d \|E_x I_\theta \psi\|^2 = 2 \int_0^{2\pi} d \|E_x I_\theta \psi\|^2 - 2 \operatorname{Re} e^{-i\theta} \int_0^{2\pi} e^{ix} \, d \|E_x I_\theta \psi\|^2$$
$$= 2 \|I_\theta \psi\|^2 - 2 \operatorname{Re} e^{-i\theta} \int_0^{2\pi} e^{ix} \, d(I_\theta \psi, E_x I_\theta \psi)$$
$$= 2 \|I_\theta \psi\|^2 - 2 \operatorname{Re} e^{-i\theta} (I_\theta \psi, U I_\theta \psi) = 0.$$

These theorems show that the jumps of E_x are the same as in the finite-dimensional case. The only difference is that in the infinite-dimensional case a continuous increase of E_x also is possible. If there are no eigenvalues and eigenvectors, then the increase of E_x is purely continuous, as in the examples A, Q, and U cited just before these theorems. If there is an orthonormal basis of eigenvectors, then E_x increases only by jumps, just as in the finite-dimensional case. Or E_x may increase both continuously and by jumps; there may be eigenvectors which span a subspace smaller than the whole space.

Let A be a self-adjoint operator and let E_x be the projection operators of its spectral decomposition. The set of points x on which E_x increases is called the *spectrum* of A. More precisely, a point is in the spectrum if it is not in an interval on which E_x is constant. The set of points x at which E_x jumps is called the *point spectrum* of A. The point spectrum is the set of all eigenvalues. The set of points x such that E_x increases continuously in the neighborhood of x is called the *continuous spectrum* of A.[14] The point spectrum and continuous spectrum together comprise the spectrum.

Similarly, if U is a unitary operator and E_x are the projection operators of its spectral decomposition, then the set of e^{ix} for which E_x is increasing is called the *spectrum* of U. The set of e^{ix} for points x at which E_x jumps is called the *point spectrum* of U. Again the point spectrum is the set of all eigenvalues. The set of e^{ix} such that E_x increases continuously in the neighborhood of x is called the *continuous spectrum* of U.[14] Again the point spectrum and continuous spectrum comprise the spectrum.

In quantum mechanics a real physical quantity is represented by a self-adjoint operator. We will see (Section 24) that the spectrum of the operator is the set of real numbers which are possible values of the quantity. The projection operators in the spectral decomposition are used to describe probability distributions of these values, discrete probability distributions over the point spectrum, and continuous probability distributions over the continuous spectrum. Thus we get a physical meaning for properties of a self-adjoint operator which can be characterized in terms of the spectrum as in the following.

Theorem 14.5. A self-adjoint operator is bounded if and only if its spectrum is bounded.

Proof. Let A be a self-adjoint operator with the spectral decomposition

$$A = \int_{-\infty}^{\infty} x \, dE_x.$$

---

[14] If E_x jumps at a point x and in addition increases continuously in the neighborhood of x, then x is in both the point spectrum and continuous spectrum of the self-adjoint operator, or e^{ix} is in both the point spectrum and continuous spectrum of the unitary operator; see Riesz and Nagy, Section 132.

In the proof of the preceding two theorems we showed that

$$(\phi, A^2\psi) = \int_{-\infty}^{\infty} x^2 \, d(\phi, E_x\psi)$$

for any vectors ψ and ϕ. Letting $\phi = \psi$ we get

$$(\phi, E_x\psi) = (\psi, E_x^2\psi) = \|E_x\psi\|^2$$

and

$$\|A\psi\|^2 = \int_{-\infty}^{\infty} x^2 \, d \|E_x\psi\|^2.$$

Suppose there is a positive number b such that the spectrum of A is in the interval $-b \le x \le b$. Then $\|E_x\psi\|^2 = 0$ for $x < -b$ and $\|E_x\psi\|^2 = \|\psi\|^2$ for $x \ge b$ and, because $\|E_x\psi\|^2$ is a monotonically increasing function of x, we have

$$\|A\psi\|^2 \le b^2 \int_{-\infty}^{\infty} d \|E_x\psi\|^2 = b^2 \|\psi\|^2.$$

Thus A is bounded; in fact, $\|A\| \le b$.

Suppose the spectrum is not bounded; just to be definite, suppose it has no upper bound. Then for each positive integer n there is an integer $m > n$ such that the projection operator $E_m - E_n$ is not zero. Let ψ be a nonzero vector such that $(E_m - E_n)\psi = \psi$. Then for $x < n$

$$E_x\psi = (E_xE_m - E_xE_n)\psi = (E_x - E_x)\psi = 0,$$

so

$$\|A\psi\|^2 \ge n^2 \int_{-\infty}^{\infty} d \|E_x\psi\|^2 = n^2 \|\psi\|^2.$$

Thus A is not bounded. This completes the proof of the theorem.

We say that a self-adjoint operator A is *positive* if $(\phi, A\phi)$ is non-negative for every vector ϕ.

Theorem 14.6. A self-adjoint operator is positive if and only if its spectrum is non-negative.

Proof. Let A be a self-adjoint operator with the spectral decomposition

$$A = \int_{-\infty}^{\infty} x \, dE_x.$$

For any vector ϕ

$$(\phi, A\phi) = \int_{-\infty}^{\infty} x \, d(\phi, E_x\phi) = \int_{-\infty}^{\infty} x \, d \|E_x\phi\|^2.$$

If the spectrum of A is non-negative, then the integral is over only non-negative x, and $(\phi, A\phi)$ is non-negative because $\|E_x\phi\|^2$ is a monotonically increasing function of x. Suppose the spectrum of A contains a negative number. Then there must be negative numbers $a < b$ such that the projection operator $E_b - E_a$ is not zero. Let ϕ be a nonzero vector such that $(E_b - E_a)\phi = \phi$. Then for $x \geq b$

$$E_x\phi = (E_xE_b - E_xE_a)\phi = (E_b - E_a)\phi = \phi,$$

so

$$(\phi, A\phi) \leq b \int_{-\infty}^{\infty} d\,\|E_x\phi\|^2 = b\,\|\phi\|^2 < 0.$$

Thus A is not positive. This completes the proof of the theorem.

15. FUNCTIONS OF AN OPERATOR, STONE'S THEOREM

The spectral decomposition is most useful when functions of an operator are considered. Let A be a self-adjoint operator with the spectral decomposition

$$A = \int_{-\infty}^{\infty} x\, dE_x.$$

Let $f(x)$ be a complex function of the real variable x. The same function of the operator A is an operator $f(A)$ defined by[15]

$$(\phi, f(A)\psi) = \int_{-\infty}^{\infty} f(x)\, d(\phi, E_x\psi)$$

for all vectors ψ and ϕ.[16] We will see that this is a reasonable definition as we consider its properties and some examples.

For $f(x) = x$ we have $f(A) = A$, because

$$\int_{-\infty}^{\infty} x\, d(\phi, E_x\psi) = (\phi, A\psi)$$

for all vectors ϕ and all vectors ψ in the domain of A. For $f(x) = 1$ we have $f(A) = 1$, because

$$\int_{-\infty}^{\infty} d(\phi, E_x\psi) = (\phi, \psi)$$

for all vectors ψ and ϕ.

---

[15] For continuous functions f these are ordinary Riemann-Stieltjes integrals; see footnote 8.
[16] If f is bounded on the spectrum of A, then this equation is for all vectors ψ and ϕ and defines $f(A)\psi$ for all vectors ψ. (See Riesz and Nagy, Section 126.) Otherwise $f(A)\psi$ is not defined for all vectors ψ, and the contents of this section have to be stated more carefully to take account of domains. (See Riesz and Nagy, Sections 127–8.)

Let $(f + g)(x) = f(x) + g(x)$ and $(cf)(x) = cf(x)$. Then

$$(f + g)(A) = f(A) + g(A)$$

and

$$(cf)(A) = cf(A).$$

Thus sums and scalar multiples of functions of an operator are defined in the natural way. So are products. Let $(fg)(x) = f(x)g(x)$. Then for any vectors ψ and ϕ

$$
(\phi, f(A)\, g(A)\psi) = \int_{-\infty}^{\infty} f(x)\, d(\phi, E_x g(A)\psi) = \int_{-\infty}^{\infty} f(x)\, d_x \int_{-\infty}^{\infty} g(y)\, d_y(E_x\phi, E_y\psi)
$$

$$
= \int_{-\infty}^{\infty} f(x)\, d \int_{-\infty}^{x} g(y)\, d(\phi, E_y\psi) = \int_{-\infty}^{\infty} f(x)g(x)\, d(\phi, E_x\psi)
$$

$$
= \int_{-\infty}^{\infty} (fg)(x)\, d(\phi, E_x\psi) = (\phi, (fg)(A)\psi),
$$

so

$$(fg)(A) = f(A)\, g(A).$$

Note that $f(A)\, g(A) = g(A)\, f(A)$; the functions of the operator A commute with each other.

From these properties we can see that polynomial functions are defined in the natural way. If

$$f(x) = c_0 + c_1 x + c_2 x^2 + \cdots + c_n x^n,$$

then[17]

$$f(A) = c_0 + c_1 A + c_2 A^2 + \cdots + c_n A^n.$$

Let $(f^*)(x) = f(x)^*$. Then for any vectors ψ and ϕ

$$
(\phi, [f(A)]^\dagger \psi) = (\psi, f(A)\phi)^* = \int_{-\infty}^{\infty} f(x)^*\, d(\psi, E_x\phi)^* = \int_{-\infty}^{\infty} (f^*)(x)\, d(\phi, E_x\psi),
$$

so $[f(A)]^\dagger = (f^*)(A)$. If f is a real function, then $f(A)$ is a self-adjoint operator. If $f^*f = 1$, then $f(A)$ is a unitary operator because $[f(A)]^\dagger f(A) = 1 = f(A)[f(A)]^\dagger$.

For any vector ϕ

$$(\phi, f(A)\phi) = \int_{-\infty}^{\infty} f(x)\, d\, \|E_x\phi\|^2.$$

It follows that $f(A)$ is positive if $f(x)$ is non-negative over the spectrum of A.

---

[17] This is true even for an unbounded operator A; see N. Dunford and J. T. Schwartz, *Linear Operators*, Part II (Interscience Publishers, New York, 1963), Corollary XII.2.8.

For any vector ψ in the domain of $f(A)$

$$\|f(A)\psi\|^2 = (\psi, [f(A)]^\dagger f(A)\psi) = (\psi, (f^*f)(A)\psi)$$

$$= \int_{-\infty}^{\infty} (f^*f)(x)\, d(\psi, E_x\psi) = \int_{-\infty}^{\infty} |f(x)|^2\, d\,\|E_x\psi\|^2.$$

It follows that $f(A)$ is bounded if $|f(x)|$ is bounded over the spectrum of A.

If A is bounded, then A^2 is a bounded positive self-adjoint operator. If A is bounded and positive, then for $f(x) = x^{\frac{1}{2}}$ we get a bounded positive self-adjoint operator $f(A) = A^{\frac{1}{2}}$ with the property that $(A^{\frac{1}{2}})^2 = A$. Thus a bounded self-adjoint operator is positive if and only if it is the square of a bounded self-adjoint operator.

Suppose A has a pure point spectrum so that

$$A = \sum_k a_k I_k,$$

where each a_k is a different eigenvalue of A and I_k is the projection operator onto the eigenvector subspace for a_k. Then for any vectors ψ and ϕ

$$(\phi, f(A)\psi) = \sum_k f(a_k)(\phi, I_k\psi),$$

so

$$f(A) = \sum_k f(a_k)I_k.$$

If $\phi_s{}^k$ are orthonormal basis vectors such that $A\phi_s{}^k = a_k\phi_s{}^k$, then $I_k\phi_s{}^j = \delta_{jk}\phi_s{}^k$ so $f(A)\phi_s{}^k = f(a_k)\phi_s{}^k$ and $(\phi_r{}^j, f(A)\phi_s{}^k) = f(a_k)\delta_{jk}\delta_{rs}$.

For an example involving a continuous spectrum consider the self-adjoint operator Q defined by $(Q\psi)(x) = x\psi(x)$ on $L^2(-\infty, \infty)$. Recall that the projection operators E_x in the spectral decomposition of Q are defined by $(E_x\psi)(y) = \psi(y)$ for $y \leq x$ and $(E_x\psi)(y) = 0$ for $y > x$. We get

$$(\phi, f(Q)\psi) = \int_{-\infty}^{\infty} f(x)\, d\int_{-\infty}^{\infty} \phi(y)^*(E_x\psi)(y)\, dy = \int_{-\infty}^{\infty} f(x)\, d\int_{-\infty}^{x} \phi(y)^*\, \psi(y)\, dy$$

$$= \int_{-\infty}^{\infty} f(x)\, \phi(x)^*\, \psi(x)\, dx = \int_{-\infty}^{\infty} \phi(x)^*\, f(x)\, \psi(x)\, dx,$$

so evidently $(f(Q)\psi)(x) = f(x)\, \psi(x)$.

We could define functions of a unitary operator in the same way, but there is no need to do so. If U is a unitary operator with the spectral decomposition

$$U = \int_0^{2\pi} e^{ix}\, dE_x,$$

then let

$$(\phi, A\psi) = \int_0^{2\pi} x\, d(\phi, E_x\psi)$$

for all vectors ψ and ϕ. This defines a bounded self-adjoint operator A whose spectral decomposition is

$$A = \int_0^{2\pi} x \, dE_x.$$

For any vectors ψ and ϕ we have

$$(\phi, U\psi) = \int_0^{2\pi} e^{ix} \, d(\phi, E_x\psi),$$

so U is a function of A, namely $U = e^{iA}$. Therefore any function of U can be considered a function of A. Evidently A is not the only Hermitian operator with the property that $U = e^{iA}$; for example, $U = e^{i(A+2\pi n)}$ for any integer n.

There is a more specific relation between Hermitian and unitary operators which is of fundamental importance for quantum mechanics. Let H be a self-adjoint operator with the spectral decomposition

$$H = \int_{-\infty}^{\infty} x \, dE_x.$$

For each real number t let

$$(\phi, U_t\psi) = \int_{-\infty}^{\infty} e^{itx} \, d(\phi, E_x\psi)$$

for all vectors ψ and ϕ. This defines an operator $U_t = e^{itH}$ which is unitary because $(e^{itx})^* e^{itx} = 1$. Evidently $U_0 = 1$. Because

$$e^{itx} e^{it'x} = e^{i(t+t')x},$$

we have

$$U_t U_{t'} = U_{t+t'}$$

for all real numbers t and t'. The converse of this is the following.

Theorem 15.1. (M. H. Stone) For each real number t let U_t be a unitary operator. Suppose $(\phi, U_t\psi)$ is a continuous function of t for all vectors ψ and ϕ. If $U_0 = 1$ and $U_t U_{t'} = U_{t+t'}$ for all real t and t', then there is a unique self-adjoint operator H such that $U_t = e^{itH}$ for all t. A vector ψ is in the domain of H if and only if the vectors $(1/it)(U_t - 1)\psi$ converge to a limit as $t \to 0$; then the limit vector is $H\psi$. If a bounded operator commutes with the unitary operators U_t, then it commutes with H.[18]

---

[18] See Riesz and Nagy, Section 137. The continuity hypothesis can be replaced by the weaker hypothesis that $(\phi, U_t\psi)$ is a Lebesgue-measurable function of t for all vectors ψ and ϕ. If H is unbounded, then commuting with H is defined for a bounded operator as in Riesz and Nagy, Section 116; it means that the bounded operator commutes with the projection operators in the spectral decomposition of H or with all bounded functions of H.

If $U_t\psi$ is in the domain of H, then

$$\frac{1}{i\,\Delta t}(U_{\Delta t} - 1)U_t\psi \to HU_t\psi$$

or

$$\frac{1}{i\,\Delta t}(U_{t+\Delta t} - U_t)\psi \to HU_t\psi$$

as $\Delta t \to 0$. We can write

$$-i\frac{d}{dt}U_t\psi = HU_t\psi.$$

16. FUNCTIONS OF COMMUTING OPERATORS

In quantum mechanics one often works with functions of two or more real variables and the corresponding functions of two or more Hermitian operators which commute with each other. Here we consider only two commuting Hermitian operators; the generalization to more than two should be obvious.

Let A be a Hermitian operator with a pure point spectrum so that

$$A = \sum_k a_k I_k,$$

where each a_k is a different eigenvalue of A and I_k is the projection operator onto the eigenvector subspace for a_k. Let B be a bounded Hermitian operator which commutes with A. For each k and any vector ψ

$$ABI_k\psi = BAI_k\psi = a_kBI_k\psi,$$

so $BI_k\psi$ is in the eigenvector subspace for a_k. Therefore

$$BI_k\psi = I_kBI_k\psi$$

for any vector ψ or

$$BI_k = I_kBI_k.$$

Taking the adjoint of both sides of this equation, we get

$$I_kB = I_kBI_k$$

and

$$I_kB = BI_k.$$

Thus each I_k commutes with every bounded Hermitian operator which commutes with A. The generalization of this for operators with both point and continuous spectra is the following.

Theorem 16.1. Let A be a self-adjoint operator with the spectral decomposition

$$A = \int_{-\infty}^{\infty} x \, dE_x.$$

If B is a bounded self-adjoint operator such that $AB = BA$ then $E_x B = BE_x$ for every x.[19]

Let A_1 and A_2 be self-adjoint operators which commute with each other and let their spectral decompositions be

$$A_1 = \int_{-\infty}^{\infty} x \, dE_x^{(1)}$$

and

$$A_2 = \int_{-\infty}^{\infty} x \, dE_x^{(2)}.$$

Then $E_x^{(1)} E_y^{(2)} = E_y^{(2)} E_x^{(1)}$ for all x and y.[20] Let $f(x, y)$ be a complex function of the two real variables x and y. The same function of the two operators A_1 and A_2 is an operator $f(A_1, A_2)$ defined by

$$(\phi, f(A_1, A_2)\psi) = \int_{-\infty}^{\infty} \int_{-\infty}^{\infty} f(x, y) \, d_x \, d_y (\phi, E_x^{(1)} E_y^{(2)} \psi)$$

for all vectors ϕ and ψ. If $f(x, y)$ depends on only one of the variables x, y, then this is the same as the previous definition of a function of a single operator. It is an easy exercise to check that sums, scalar multiples, and products of functions are defined in the natural way and that

$$[f(A_1, A_2)]^\dagger = (f^*)(A_1, A_2),$$

where

$$(f^*)(x, y) = f(x, y)^*.$$

(One needs to use the fact that $E_x^{(1)}$ and $E_y^{(2)}$ commute.) It follows that all functions of A_1 and A_2 commute with each other, that polynomial functions are defined in the natural way, that real functions $f(x, y)$ define self-adjoint operators $f(A_1, A_2)$, that non-negative functions define positive operators, and that unitary operators $f(A_1, A_2)$ are defined by functions $f(x, y)$ for which $f^*f = 1$. This is the same as for functions of a single operator.

---

[19] For an unbounded operator A this theorem and the preceding discussion have to be stated more carefully to take account of domains. See Stone, Chapter 8, Section 1 or Riesz and Nagy, Sections 107, 116, and 120.
[20] This follows from a double application of Theorem 16.1 if either A_1 or A_2 is bounded; see footnote 19. When both A_1 and A_2 are unbounded, we simply take it as the definition which gives precise meaning to the statement that A_1 commutes with A_2.

Suppose A_1 and A_2 have pure point spectra so that

$$A_r = \sum_k a_k^{(r)} I_k^{(r)}$$

for $r = 1, 2$, where each $a_k^{(r)}$ is a different eigenvalue of A_r and $I_k^{(r)}$ is the projection operator onto the eigenvector subspace for $a_k^{(r)}$. Then

$$f(A_1, A_2) = \sum_{jk} f(a_j^{(1)}, a_k^{(2)}) I_j^{(1)} I_k^{(2)}.$$

For an example involving continuous spectra consider the space L^2 of square-integrable functions $\psi(\mathbf{x}) = \psi(x_1, x_2, x_3)$ with inner product

$$(\phi, \psi) = \int \phi(\mathbf{x})^* \psi(\mathbf{x}) \, d\mathbf{x}.$$

For each $r = 1, 2, 3$ let $(Q_r \psi)(\mathbf{x}) = x_r \psi(\mathbf{x})$. This defines a self-adjoint operator Q_r. The projection operators $E_x^{(r)}$ in the spectral decomposition

$$Q_r = \int_{-\infty}^{\infty} x \, dE_x^{(r)}$$

are defined by $(E_x^{(r)} \psi)(\mathbf{y}) = \psi(\mathbf{y})$ for $y_r \leq x$ and $(E_x^{(r)} \psi)(\mathbf{y}) = 0$ for $y_r > x$. A calculation similar to that for the one-dimensional case yields

$$(f(Q_1, Q_2, Q_3)\psi)(\mathbf{x}) = f(x_1, x_2, x_3)\psi(\mathbf{x}).$$

17. COMPLETE SETS OF COMMUTING OPERATORS, SPECTRAL REPRESENTATION

Let $A_1, A_2, \ldots, A_N$ be mutually commuting Hermitian operators with pure point spectra. Then for each $r = 1, 2, \ldots, N$

$$A_r = \sum_k a_k^{(r)} I_k^{(r)},$$

where each $a_k^{(r)}$ is a different eigenvalue of A_r and $I_k^{(r)}$ is the projection operator onto the subspace spanned by the eigenvectors of A_r for $a_k^{(r)}$. From the preceding section we know that the projection operators $I_k^{(r)}$ commute with each other for all different r and k;

$$I_j^{(r)} I_k^{(s)} = I_k^{(s)} I_j^{(r)}.$$

It follows that

$$I_j^{(1)} I_k^{(2)} \cdots I_l^{(N)}$$

is a projection operator for any $j, k, \ldots, l$. It projects onto the subspace of all vectors ψ such that $A_1 \psi = a_j^{(1)} \psi$ and $A_2 \psi = a_k^{(2)} \psi \cdots$ and $A_N \psi = a_l^{(N)} \psi$.

These projection operators are mutually orthogonal,

$$I_j^{(1)} I_k^{(2)} \cdots I_l^{(N)} I_{j'}^{(1)} I_{k'}^{(2)} \cdots I_{l'}^{(N)} = \delta_{jj'} \delta_{kk'} \cdots \delta_{ll'} I_j^{(1)} I_k^{(2)} \cdots I_l^{(N)},$$

and they have the completeness property that

$$\sum_j \sum_k \cdots \sum_l I_j^{(1)} I_k^{(2)} \cdots I_l^{(N)} = 1.$$

Some of these projection operators may be zero. Suppose none of them projects onto a subspace of dimension larger than one. Then we say that the set of operators $A_1, A_2, \ldots, A_N$ is a *complete set of commuting operators*. For each nonzero projection operator $I_j^{(1)} I_k^{(2)} \cdots I_l^{(N)}$ let $|a_j^{(1)}, a_k^{(2)}, \ldots, a_l^{(N)}\rangle$ be a vector of length one such that

$$I_j^{(1)} I_k^{(2)} \cdots I_l^{(N)} = |a_j^{(1)}, a_k^{(2)}, \cdots, a_l^{(N)}\rangle \langle a_j^{(1)}, a_k^{(2)}, \cdots, a_l^{(N)}|.$$

The set of all these vectors is an orthonormal basis. Each vector $|a_j^{(1)}, a_k^{(2)}, \ldots, a_l^{(N)}\rangle$ is an eigenvector of $A_1, A_2, \ldots, A_N$ and is labeled completely by the eigenvalues $a_j^{(1)}, a_k^{(2)}, \ldots, a_l^{(N)}$.

Given a set of commuting Hermitian operators with pure point spectra we can always get a complete set of commuting operators by adding one more operator to the set. For example, suppose A_1 and A_2 are given. For each nonzero projection operator $I_j^{(1)} I_k^{(2)}$ let $|a_j^{(1)}, a_k^{(2)}, a_l^{(3)}\rangle$ be orthonormal vectors such that

$$I_j^{(1)} I_k^{(2)} = \sum_{a_l^{(3)}} |a_j^{(1)}, a_k^{(2)}, a_l^{(3)}\rangle \langle a_j^{(1)}, a_k^{(2)}, a_l^{(3)}|.$$

The set of all these vectors is an orthonormal basis. The labels $a_l^{(3)}$ should be real numbers which, with the eigenvalues $a_j^{(1)}$ and $a_k^{(2)}$, are sufficient to distinguish the different vectors. Let

$$A_3 |a_j^{(1)}, a_k^{(2)}, a_l^{(3)}\rangle = a_l^{(3)} |a_j^{(1)}, a_k^{(2)}, a_l^{(3)}\rangle.$$

This defines a Hermitian operator A_3 with a pure point spectrum, which commutes with A_1 and A_2. The set of operators A_1, A_2, A_3 is a complete set of commuting operators.

An alternative definition of a complete set of commuting operators is provided by the following.

Theorem 17.1. Let $A_1, A_2, \ldots, A_N$ be mutually commuting Hermitian operators with pure point spectra. This is a complete set of commuting operators if and only if every bounded operator which commutes with all the operators $A_1, A_2, \ldots, A_N$ is a function of the operators $A_1, A_2, \ldots, A_N$.

Proof. Suppose $A_1, A_2, \ldots, A_N$ is a complete set of commuting operators. Let B be a bounded operator which commutes with $A_1, A_2, \ldots, A_N$. For each eigenvector $|a_j^{(1)}, \ldots, a_k^{(r)}, \ldots, a_l^{(N)}\rangle$

$$A_r B \,|a_j^{(1)}, \ldots, a_k^{(r)}, \ldots, a_l^{(N)}\rangle = BA_r \,|a_j^{(1)}, \ldots, a_k^{(r)}, \ldots, a_l^{(N)}\rangle$$
$$= a_k^{(r)} B \,|a_j^{(1)}, \ldots, a_k^{(r)}, \ldots, a_l^{(N)}\rangle$$

for all $r = 1, 2, \ldots, N$. For each set of eigenvalues $a_j^{(1)}, \ldots, a_k^{(r)}, \ldots, a_l^{(N)}$ there is not more than one linearly independent eigenvector of $A_1, A_2, \ldots, A_N$. Therefore

$$B \,|a_j^{(1)}, \ldots, a_k^{(r)}, \ldots, a_l^{(N)}\rangle$$
$$= f(a_j^{(1)}, \ldots, a_k^{(r)}, \ldots, a_l^{(N)}) \,|a_j^{(1)}, \ldots, a_k^{(r)}, \ldots, a_l^{(N)}\rangle$$

where $f(a_j^{(1)}, \ldots, a_k^{(r)}, \ldots, a_l^{(N)})$ is a complex function of the eigenvalues. Thus

$$B = f(A_1, \ldots, A_r, \ldots, A_N).$$

Suppose $A_1, A_2, \ldots, A_N$ is not a complete set of commuting operators. Then for some set of eigenvalues $a_j^{(1)}, a_k^{(2)}, \ldots, a_l^{(N)}$ the subspace spanned by the eigenvectors of $A_1, A_2, \ldots, A_N$ has dimension larger than one. Let B be a bounded operator which is reduced by this subspace, is zero on its orthogonal complement, but is not a scalar multiple of the projection operator onto this subspace. Then B commutes with $A_1, A_2, \ldots, A_N$ but is not a function of $A_1, A_2, \ldots, A_N$. This completes the proof of the theorem.

The orthonormal basis of eigenvectors $|a_j^{(1)}, a_k^{(2)}, \ldots, a_l^{(N)}\rangle$ is very useful for working with the complete set of commuting operators $A_1, A_2, \ldots, A_N$. With respect to this basis the Hilbert space is identified with a space l^2 in which a vector ψ has components $\langle a_j^{(1)}, a_k^{(2)}, \ldots, a_l^{(N)} \,|\, \psi\rangle$ and a vector $A_r\psi$ has components

$$\langle a_j^{(1)}, \ldots, a_k^{(r)}, \ldots, a_l^{(N)} \,|\, A_r\psi\rangle = a_k^{(r)} \langle a_j^{(1)}, \ldots, a_k^{(r)}, \ldots, a_l^{(N)} \,|\, \psi\rangle$$

for $r = 1, 2, \ldots, N$. In fact for any function f of $A_1, A_2, \ldots, A_N$ a vector $f(A_1, A_2, \ldots, A_N)\psi$ has components

$$\langle a_j^{(1)}, a_k^{(2)}, \ldots, a_l^{(N)} \,|\, f(A_1, A_2, \ldots, A_N)\psi\rangle$$
$$= f(a_j^{(1)}, a_k^{(2)}, \ldots, a_l^{(N)}) \langle a_j^{(1)}, a_k^{(2)}, \ldots, a_l^{(N)} \,|\, \psi\rangle.$$

Thus all of these operators are represented by diagonal matrices. This is called the *spectral representation* of the complete set of commuting operators $A_1, A_2, \ldots, A_N$.

For operators with continuous spectra a complete set of commuting operators is defined by the property that any bounded operator which commutes with them is a function of them. But the spectral representation is the property which is most useful in quantum mechanics, and in general the spectral representation is quite complicated for operators with continuous spectra.[21] Therefore we consider only some simple examples for which the spectral representation is of the kind generally used in quantum mechanics.

Consider the space $L^2(-\infty, \infty)$ and the set of commuting Hermitian operators which consists of the single operator Q defined by $(Q\psi)(x) = x\,\psi(x)$. That this is a complete set of commuting operators is established by the following.

Theorem 17.2. Every bounded operator which commutes[22] with Q is a function of Q.

Proof. Let ψ be a vector such that $\psi(x)$ is positive for all x. For any vector ϕ let $g(x) = \phi(x)/\psi(x)$. Then

$$\phi(x) = g(x)\,\psi(x) = (g(Q)\psi)(x)$$

or $\phi = g(Q)\psi$. If B is a bounded operator which commutes with Q, then B commutes with $g(Q)$,[22] so $B\phi = g(Q)B\psi$ or

$$(B\phi)(x) = g(x)(B\psi)(x) = \frac{\phi(x)(B\psi)(x)}{\psi(x)}.$$

Let $f(x) = (B\psi)(x)/\psi(x)$. Then

$$(B\psi)(x) = f(x)\,\psi(x) = (f(Q)\psi)(x)$$

and

$$(B\phi)(x) = f(x)\,\phi(x) = (f(Q)\phi)(x).$$

Thus $B = f(Q)$. This completes the proof.

The spectrum of Q is purely continuous and consists of all real numbers x. Each vector ψ is a function $\psi(x)$ on the spectrum of Q. To bring out the analogy with a complete set of commuting operators with pure point spectra we write

$$\langle x \mid \psi \rangle = \psi(x).$$

Then

$$\langle x \mid Q\psi \rangle = x \langle x \mid \psi \rangle.$$

This is the spectral representation of Q. For a function f of Q we have

$$\langle x \mid f(Q)\psi \rangle = f(x) \langle x \mid \psi \rangle.$$

We would have a more complete analogy with point spectra if we could write

$$Q \mid x \rangle = x \mid x \rangle.$$

---

[21] See J. M. Jauch and B. Misra, *Helv. Phys. Acta* **38**, 30 (1965).
[22] This should be stated more carefully to take account of domains; see Riesz and Nagy, Sections 116, 127, and 128.

But Q has no eigenvectors; if ψ is a vector such that $Q\psi = a\psi$ for a real number a, then ψ is the zero vector; if $x\psi(x) = a\psi(x)$, then $\psi(x)$ is zero for $x \neq a$ and

$$\|\psi\|^2 = \int_{-\infty}^{\infty} |\psi(x)|^2 \, dx = 0,$$

because the Lebesgue integral is not changed by the value of the integrand at a single point.[23] Nevertheless, we can use delta functions for eigenfunctions of Q as follows. For each real number a

$$x\delta(x - a) = a\delta(x - a).$$

If we write $|a\rangle$ for $\delta(x - a)$, we can write

$$Q\,|a\rangle = a\,|a\rangle.$$

We do not use $\delta(x - a)$ as a Lebesgue-square-integrable function, so we do not think of $|a\rangle$ as a vector in the Hilbert space L^2. We handle them according to the rules for using delta functions.[24] In this sense we have

$$\langle a \mid \psi \rangle = \psi(a) = \int_{-\infty}^{\infty} \delta(x - a)\psi(x) \, dx$$

for the components of a vector ψ in the spectral representation of Q. We can think of these as the inner products of ψ with the delta functions. We also have

$$\psi(x) = \int_{-\infty}^{\infty} \psi(a)\delta(x - a) \, da,$$

which we can write as

$$|\psi\rangle = \int_{-\infty}^{\infty} \langle a \mid \psi \rangle \, |a\rangle \, da,$$

so we can think of any vector ψ as a linear combination of delta functions. Thus the delta functions are analogous to an orthonormal basis of eigenvectors.

For each real number a let $|a\rangle\langle a|$ be defined by

$$(|a\rangle\langle a|\psi)(x) = \psi(a)\delta(x - a)$$

or

$$|a\rangle\langle a|\psi = \langle a \mid \psi \rangle \, |a\rangle.$$

[23] See Section 2, *Inner Products*, particularly footnote 7.
[24] Dirac, Section 15; A. Messiah, *Quantum Mechanics*, Vol. I (North-Holland Publishing Co., Amsterdam; John Wiley and Sons, New York; 1961), Appendix A; J. P. Marchand, *Distributions* (North-Holland Publishing Co., Amsterdam; Interscience Publishers, New York; 1962).

For the projection operators E_x in the spectral decomposition of Q we have

$$(E_x \psi)(y) = \int_{-\infty}^{x} \psi(a)\delta(y - a)\, da,$$

which we can write as

$$(E_x \psi)(y) = \int_{-\infty}^{x} (|a\rangle\langle a|\psi)(y)\, da$$

for any vector ψ or

$$E_x = \int_{-\infty}^{x} |a\rangle\langle a|\, da.$$

Then for the spectral decomposition

$$Q = \int_{-\infty}^{\infty} x\, dE_x$$

we can write

$$Q = \int_{-\infty}^{\infty} x\, |x\rangle\langle x|\, dx.$$

This is analogous to a sum of eigenvalues multiplying projection operators onto eigenvector subspaces.

Consider the space L^2 of square-integrable functions $\psi(\mathbf{x}) = \psi(x_1, x_2, x_3)$ and the commuting Hermitian operators $\mathbf{Q} = (Q_1, Q_2, Q_3)$ defined by $(Q_r \psi)(\mathbf{x}) = x_r\, \psi(\mathbf{x})$ for $r = 1, 2, 3$, or $(\mathbf{Q}\psi)(\mathbf{x}) = \mathbf{x}\, \psi(\mathbf{x})$. This is a complete set of commuting operators. Every bounded operator which commutes with Q_1, Q_2, Q_3 is a function of Q_1, Q_2, Q_3. The proof is the same as for the single operator Q above.

Each of the operators Q_1, Q_2, Q_3 has a purely continuous spectrum which consists of all real numbers. A vector ψ is a function $\psi(x_1, x_2, x_3)$ on the spectra of Q_1, Q_2, Q_3. For the spectral representation of Q_1, Q_2, Q_3 we can write

$$\langle x_1, x_2, x_3 \mid \psi \rangle = \psi(x_1, x_2, x_3)$$

or

$$\langle \mathbf{x} \mid \psi \rangle = \psi(\mathbf{x})$$

and

$$\langle x_1, x_2, x_3 \mid Q_r \psi \rangle = x_r \langle x_1, x_2, x_3 \mid \psi \rangle$$

for $r = 1, 2, 3$, or

$$\langle \mathbf{x} \mid \mathbf{Q}\psi \rangle = \mathbf{x}\, \langle \mathbf{x} \mid \psi \rangle.$$

For a function f of Q_1, Q_2, Q_3 we have

$$\langle x_1, x_2, x_3 \mid f(Q_1, Q_2, Q_3)\psi \rangle = f(x_1, x_2, x_3)\, \langle x_1, x_2, x_3 \mid \psi \rangle$$

or

$$\langle \mathbf{x} \mid f(\mathbf{Q})\psi \rangle = f(\mathbf{x})\, \langle \mathbf{x} \mid \psi \rangle.$$

The operators $\mathbf{Q}$ have no eigenvectors, but we can use delta functions as analogs of eigenvectors just as for the single operator Q discussed above. If we write $|\mathbf{a}\rangle$ for $\delta(\mathbf{x} - \mathbf{a})$, we can write

$$\mathbf{Q}|\mathbf{a}\rangle = \mathbf{a}|\mathbf{a}\rangle$$

for

$$\mathbf{x}\delta(\mathbf{x} - \mathbf{a}) = \mathbf{a}\delta(\mathbf{x} - \mathbf{a}).$$

For the components of a vector ψ in the spectral representation of the operators $\mathbf{Q}$ we have

$$\langle \mathbf{a} \mid \psi \rangle = \psi(\mathbf{a}) = \int \delta(\mathbf{x} - \mathbf{a})\psi(\mathbf{x})\,d\mathbf{x}.$$

These are analogous to inner products. For

$$\psi(\mathbf{x}) = \int \psi(\mathbf{a})\delta(\mathbf{x} - \mathbf{a})\,d\mathbf{a}$$

we can write

$$|\psi\rangle = \int \langle \mathbf{a} \mid \psi \rangle |\mathbf{a}\rangle\,d\mathbf{a},$$

which is analogous to writing ψ as a linear combination of orthonormal basis vectors. For the projection operators $E_x^{(r)}$ in the spectral decomposition of Q_r we can write

$$E_x^{(r)} = \int_{a_r \leq x} |\mathbf{a}\rangle\langle \mathbf{a}|\,d\mathbf{a}.$$

Then for the spectral decomposition of the operators $\mathbf{Q}$ we get

$$\mathbf{Q} = \int \mathbf{x}|\mathbf{x}\rangle\langle \mathbf{x}|\,d\mathbf{x},$$

which is analogous to spectral decompositions in terms of eigenvalues and eigenvectors.

18.   FOURIER TRANSFORMS, SPECTRAL REPRESENTATION OF $-i\nabla$

Consider again the space L^2 of square-integrable functions $\psi(\mathbf{x}) = \psi(x_1, x_2, x_3)$. For each $r = 1, 2, 3$ let

$$(P_r\psi)(\mathbf{x}) = -i\frac{\partial}{\partial x_r}\,\psi(\mathbf{x}).$$

This defines three self-adjoint operators $\mathbf{P} = (P_1, P_2, P_3)$.[25] We can write

$$(\mathbf{P}\psi)(\mathbf{x}) = -i\nabla\psi(\mathbf{x}).$$

The spectral representation of these operators is provided by Fourier transforms.

Theorem 18.1. If ψ is a vector in L^2, then

$$\chi_n(\mathbf{k}) = (2\pi)^{-\frac{3}{2}} \int_{-n}^{n} dx_1 \int_{-n}^{n} dx_2 \int_{-n}^{n} dx_3 e^{-i\mathbf{k}\cdot\mathbf{x}} \psi(\mathbf{x})$$

defines a sequence of vectors χ_n in L^2 which converges as $n \to \infty$ to a limit vector $F\psi$ such that $\|F\psi\|^2 = \|\psi\|^2$, and

$$\psi_n(\mathbf{x}) = (2\pi)^{-\frac{3}{2}} \int_{-n}^{n} dk_1 \int_{-n}^{n} dk_2 \int_{-n}^{n} dk_3 (F\psi)(\mathbf{k}) e^{i\mathbf{k}\cdot\mathbf{x}}$$

defines a sequence of vectors ψ_n which converges to ψ as $n \to \infty$.[26] A vector ψ is in the domain of P_r if and only if $k_r(F\psi)(\mathbf{k})$ is square-integrable; then

$$(FP_r\psi)(\mathbf{k}) = k_r(F\psi)(\mathbf{k}).\text{[27]}$$

We write

$$(F\psi)(\mathbf{k}) = (2\pi)^{-\frac{3}{2}} \int e^{-i\mathbf{k}\cdot\mathbf{x}} \psi(\mathbf{x}) \, d\mathbf{x}$$

and

$$\psi(\mathbf{x}) = (2\pi)^{-\frac{3}{2}} \int (F\psi)(\mathbf{k}) e^{i\mathbf{k}\cdot\mathbf{x}} \, d\mathbf{k}.$$

We call $F\psi$ the *Fourier transform* of ψ. Evidently F is a unitary operator on L^2. For its inverse we can write

$$(F^{-1}\phi)(\mathbf{x}) = (2\pi)^{-\frac{3}{2}} \int \phi(\mathbf{k}) e^{i\mathbf{k}\cdot\mathbf{x}} \, d\mathbf{k}$$

or

$$(F^{-1}\phi)(\mathbf{x}) = (F\phi)(-\mathbf{x})$$

for every vector ϕ. Since F is unitary, it preserves inner products as well as lengths of vectors; we have

$$\int (F\phi)(\mathbf{k})^*(F\psi)(\mathbf{k}) \, d\mathbf{k} = \int \phi(\mathbf{x})^* \psi(\mathbf{x}) \, d\mathbf{x}$$

---

[25] That $(\phi, P_r\psi) = (P_r\phi, \psi)$ can be seen by integrating by parts for vectors ψ and ϕ in the domain of P_r. But P_r is an unbounded operator, so one must show that P_r has a dense domain to define $P_r{}^\dagger$ and then show that $P_r = P_r{}^\dagger$. See Stone, Theorem 10.9.

[26] See Stone, Theorem 3.10, or Riesz and Nagy, Sections 112 and 113.

[27] See Stone, Theorem 10.9.

for all vectors ψ and ϕ. For $P_r\psi$ we can write

$$(P_r\psi)(\mathbf{x}) = (2\pi)^{-3/2}\int (F\psi)(\mathbf{k})k_r e^{i\mathbf{k}\cdot\mathbf{x}}\,d\mathbf{k}$$

or

$$-i\nabla\psi(\mathbf{x}) = (2\pi)^{-3/2}\int (F\psi)(\mathbf{k})\mathbf{k}e^{i\mathbf{k}\cdot\mathbf{x}}\,d\mathbf{k}.$$

In terms of the three operators $\mathbf{Q} = (Q_1, Q_2, Q_3)$ defined by $(Q_r\psi)(\mathbf{x}) = x_r\,\psi(\mathbf{x})$ we have

$$FP_r = Q_r F$$

for $r = 1, 2, 3$ or

$$\mathbf{P} = F^{-1}\mathbf{Q}F.$$

From the spectral decomposition

$$Q_r = \int_{-\infty}^{\infty} x\,dE_x^{(r)}$$

we obtain the spectral decomposition of P_r. The set of operators $F^{-1}E_x^{(r)}F$ is a spectral family of projection operators; it is an easy exercise to check that this follows simply because F is unitary and the set of operators $E_x^{(r)}$ is a spectral family of projection operators. Since $F^{-1} = F^\dagger$, we have

$$(\phi, P_r\psi) = (\phi, F^\dagger Q_r F\psi) = (F\phi, Q_r F\psi)$$
$$= \int_{-\infty}^{\infty} x\,d(F\phi, E_x^{(r)} F\psi) = \int_{-\infty}^{\infty} x\,d(\phi, F^{-1}E_x^{(r)} F\psi)$$

for any vector ϕ and any vector ψ in the domain of P_r. Thus the spectral decomposition of P_r is

$$P_r = \int_{-\infty}^{\infty} x\,dF^{-1}E_x^{(r)}F.$$

Recall that $E_x^{(r)}$ is the projection operator onto the subspace of all vectors ψ such that $\psi(\mathbf{x}) = 0$ for $x_r > x$. Therefore $F^{-1}E_x^{(r)}F$ is the projection operator onto the subspace of all vectors ψ such that $(F\psi)(\mathbf{k}) = 0$ for $k_r > x$. Evidently P_r has the same spectrum as Q_r, namely a purely continuous spectrum consisting of all real numbers.

Functions of the operators P_1, P_2, P_3 are defined by integrals with respect to inner products

$$(\phi, F^{-1}E_x^{(1)}FF^{-1}E_y^{(2)}FF^{-1}E_z^{(3)} F\psi) = (F\phi, E_x^{(1)}E_y^{(2)}E_z^{(3)} F\psi).$$

Thus for any complex function $f(\mathbf{x}) = f(x, y, z)$, the operator $f(\mathbf{P}) = f(P_1, P_2, P_3)$ is determined by inner products

$$(\phi, f(\mathbf{P})\psi) = \int_{-\infty}^{\infty} \int_{-\infty}^{\infty} \int_{-\infty}^{\infty} f(x, y, z)\, d_x\, d_y\, d_z (F\phi, E_x^{(1)} E_y^{(2)} E_z^{(3)}\, F\psi)$$

$$= (F\phi, f(Q_1, Q_2, Q_3)F\psi) = (\phi, F^{-1} f(\mathbf{Q})F\psi).$$

Therefore $f(\mathbf{P}) = F^{-1} f(\mathbf{Q})F$. We can write

$$(Ff(\mathbf{P})\psi)(\mathbf{k}) = f(\mathbf{k})(F\psi)(\mathbf{k})$$

or

$$(f(\mathbf{P})\psi)(\mathbf{x}) = (2\pi)^{-\frac{3}{2}} \int (F\psi)(\mathbf{k})\, f(\mathbf{k}) e^{i\mathbf{k}\cdot\mathbf{x}}\, d\mathbf{k}.$$

Because Q_1, Q_2, Q_3 is a complete set of commuting operators, P_1, P_2, P_3 also is a complete set of commuting operators. If B is a bounded operator which commutes with the three operators $\mathbf{P}$, then FBF^{-1} is a bounded operator which commutes with the three operators $FPF^{-1} = \mathbf{Q}$, so there is a function f of three real variables such that $FBF^{-1} = f(\mathbf{Q})$ and

$$B = F^{-1}f(\mathbf{Q})F = f(\mathbf{P}).$$

We have been thinking of the Fourier transformation as an operator F which takes a vector ψ to a different vector $F\psi$. We may also think of $\psi(\mathbf{x})$ and $(F\psi)(\mathbf{k})$ as two different ways of representing the same vector ψ as a function. We can write

$$\langle k_1, k_2, k_3 \mid \psi \rangle = (F\psi)(k_1, k_2, k_3)$$

or

$$\langle \mathbf{k} \mid \psi \rangle = (F\psi)(\mathbf{k}),$$

provided we are careful not to confuse this with

$$\langle \mathbf{x} \mid \psi \rangle = \psi(\mathbf{x}).$$

We think of $\langle k_1, k_2, k_3 \mid \psi \rangle$ as a function on the spectra of P_1, P_2, P_3. We have

$$\langle k_1, k_2, k_3 \mid P_r\psi \rangle = k_r \langle k_1, k_2, k_3 \mid \psi \rangle$$

for $r = 1, 2, 3$, or

$$\langle \mathbf{k} \mid \mathbf{P}\psi \rangle = \mathbf{k}\langle \mathbf{k} \mid \psi \rangle.$$

This is the spectral representation of P_1, P_2, P_3. For a function f of P_1, P_2, P_3 we have

$$\langle k_1, k_2, k_3 \mid f(P_1, P_2, P_3)\psi \rangle = f(k_1, k_2, k_3)\, \langle k_1, k_2, k_3 \mid \psi \rangle$$

or

$$\langle \mathbf{k} \mid f(\mathbf{P})\psi \rangle = f(\mathbf{k})\, \langle \mathbf{k} \mid \psi \rangle.$$

The operators $\mathbf{P}$ have no eigenvectors, but they have eigenfunctions which we can use as analogs of eigenvectors. If we write $|\mathbf{k}\rangle$ for $(2\pi)^{-3/2}e^{i\mathbf{k}\cdot\mathbf{x}}$, we can write

$$\mathbf{P}\,|\mathbf{k}\rangle = \mathbf{k}\,|\mathbf{k}\rangle$$

for

$$-i\nabla(2\pi)^{-3/2}e^{i\mathbf{k}\cdot\mathbf{x}} = \mathbf{k}(2\pi)^{-3/2}e^{i\mathbf{k}\cdot\mathbf{x}}.$$

For the components of a vector ψ in the spectral representation of the operators $\mathbf{P}$ we have

$$\langle\mathbf{k}\mid\psi\rangle = (F\psi)(\mathbf{k}) = \int [(2\pi)^{-3/2}e^{i\mathbf{k}\cdot\mathbf{x}}]^*\;\psi(\mathbf{x})\;d\mathbf{x}.$$

We can think of these as the inner products of ψ with the eigenfunctions $(2\pi)^{-3/2}e^{i\mathbf{k}\cdot\mathbf{x}}$. We have also

$$\psi(\mathbf{x}) = \int (F\psi)(\mathbf{k})(2\pi)^{-3/2}e^{i\mathbf{k}\cdot\mathbf{x}}d\mathbf{k},$$

which we can write as

$$|\psi\rangle = \int \langle\mathbf{k}\mid\psi\rangle\,|\mathbf{k}\rangle\,d\mathbf{k},$$

so we can think of any vector ψ as a linear combination of the eigenfunctions. Thus the eigenfunctions $(2\pi)^{-3/2}e^{i\mathbf{k}\cdot\mathbf{x}}$ are analogous to an orthonormal basis of eigenvectors. They are not vectors in the Hilbert space L^2 because they are not square integrable. Using them is much the same as using delta functions for eigenfunctions of the operators $\mathbf{Q}$. Indeed

$$(2\pi)^{-3/2}e^{i\mathbf{k}\cdot\mathbf{x}} = (2\pi)^{-3/2}\int \delta(\mathbf{k}' - \mathbf{k})e^{i\mathbf{k}'\cdot\mathbf{x}}\,d\mathbf{k}'$$

is the inverse Fourier transform of a delta function.

Let $|\mathbf{k}\rangle\langle\mathbf{k}|$ be defined by

$$(|\mathbf{k}\rangle\langle\mathbf{k}|\psi)(\mathbf{x}) = (F\psi)(\mathbf{k})(2\pi)^{-3/2}e^{i\mathbf{k}\cdot\mathbf{x}}$$

or

$$|\mathbf{k}\rangle\langle\mathbf{k}|\psi = \langle\mathbf{k}\mid\psi\rangle\,|\mathbf{k}\rangle.$$

Then for the projection operators $F^{-1}E_x^{(r)}F$ in the spectral decomposition of P_r we can write

$$(F^{-1}E_x^{(r)}F\psi)(\mathbf{y}) = \int_{k_r \le x} (F\psi)(\mathbf{k})(2\pi)^{-3/2}e^{i\mathbf{k}\cdot\mathbf{y}}\,d\mathbf{k}$$

$$= \int_{k_r \le x} (|\mathbf{k}\rangle\langle\mathbf{k}|\psi)(\mathbf{y})\,d\mathbf{k}$$

or

$$F^{-1}E_x^{(r)}F = \int_{k_r \leq x} |\mathbf{k}\rangle\langle\mathbf{k}|\, d\mathbf{k},$$

and for the spectral decomposition of the operators $\mathbf{P}$ we get

$$\mathbf{P} = \int \mathbf{k}\, |\mathbf{k}\rangle\langle\mathbf{k}|\, d\mathbf{k},$$

which is analogous to spectral decompositions in terms of eigenvalues and eigenvectors.

See *Exercises and Applications* 2, 3, 4, 5, and 8.

4

OPERATOR ALGEBRAS

We use operator algebras to describe general properties of functions of non-commuting operators, for example to say which operators are functions of a given set of noncommuting operators. In particular we find general conditions under which the functions of a set of noncommuting operators include all bounded operators. We again consider operators on a complex separable Hilbert space.

19. IRREDUCIBLE OPERATORS, SCHUR'S LEMMA

We say that a set of operators is *reducible* if there is a subspace, other than the whole space or the subspace containing only the zero vector, which reduces every operator in the set.[1] If a set of operators is not reducible, we say it is *irreducible*. We say that a subspace $\mathcal{M}$ is *invariant* under a set of operators if $A\psi$ is in $\mathcal{M}$ for every operator A in the set and every vector ψ in $\mathcal{M}$.[2] Evidently a subspace $\mathcal{M}$ reduces a set of operators if and only if $\mathcal{M}$ and $\mathcal{M}^{\perp}$ are invariant under the set of operators. We say that a set of operators is *symmetric* if $A^{\dagger}$ is in the set for every operator A in the set; for example, a set of Hermitian operators is symmetric.

Theorem 19.1.   If a subspace is invariant under a symmetric set of operators, then it reduces the set of operators (in other words, its orthogonal complement also is invariant).

[1] See Section 12, *Eigenvalues and Eigenvectors*, particularly Theorem 12.7.
[2] For unbounded operators these definitions have to be stated more carefully to take account of domains and to get the following theorem; see Riesz and Nagy, Sections 115–117 and Stone, Chapter IV, Section 3.

Proof. Let $\mathcal{M}$ be the subspace which is invariant under the set of operators and let E be the projection operator onto $\mathcal{M}$. Let A be an operator in the set. Then $AE\psi$ is in $\mathcal{M}$, so

$$AE\psi = EAE\psi$$

for every vector ψ, or

$$AE = EAE.$$

Because the set of operators is symmetric, $A^\dagger$ is in the set and

$$A^\dagger E = EA^\dagger E.$$

Taking the adjoint, we have

$$EA = EAE.$$

Therefore

$$EA = AE.$$

This implies that $\mathcal{M}$ reduces A.[1]

Theorem 19.2.   (Schur's Lemma)   A symmetric set of bounded or Hermitian operators is irreducible if and only if multiples of the identity operator are the only bounded operators which commute with all operators in the set.

Proof. Suppose $\mathcal{M}$ is a subspace which reduces the set of operators. Let E be the projection operator onto $\mathcal{M}$. Then E commutes with all operators in the set.[1] If multiples of the identity operator are the only bounded operators which commute with all operators in the set, then E is either the identity operator or zero, and $\mathcal{M}$ is either the whole space or the subspace containing only the zero vector, so the set of operators is irreducible.

Suppose the set of operators is irreducible. Let E be a projection operator which commutes with every operator in the set. Then E projects onto a subspace which reduces the set of operators, so this subspace is either the whole space or the subspace containing only the zero vector. Therefore E is either the identity operator or zero.

Let B be a bounded Hermitian operator which commutes with every operator in the set. Then each of the projection operators E_x in the spectral decomposition of B commutes with every operator in the set.[3] Therefore E_x is either the identity operator or zero; there is a real number b such that $E_x = 0$ for $x < b$ and $E_x = 1$ for $x \geq b$. It follows that

$$(\phi, B\psi) = \int_{-\infty}^{\infty} x \, d(\phi, E_x\psi) = b(\phi, \psi) = (\phi, b\psi)$$

---

[3] From Section 16, *Functions of Commuting Operators*, we know that if a Hermitian operator commutes with B, then it commutes with E_x. If A is a bounded non-Hermitian operator which commutes with B, then taking the adjoint of $AB = BA$ yields $BA^\dagger = A^\dagger B$, so B commutes with Re A and Im A. Therefore E_x commutes with Re A and Im A, so E_x commutes with A.

for all vectors ψ and ϕ, so $B\psi = b\psi$ for all vectors ψ. Thus B is a multiple of the identity operator.

Let B be a bounded non-Hermitian operator which commutes with every operator in the set. If A is in the set, then $A^\dagger$ is in the set and B commutes with $A^\dagger$. Taking the adjoint of $BA^\dagger = A^\dagger B$ yields $AB^\dagger = B^\dagger A$, so $B^\dagger$ commutes with every operator in the set.[4] It follows that Re B and Im B commute with every operator in the set. Therefore Re B and Im B are multiples of the identity operator, so $B = $ Re $B + i$ Im B is a multiple of the identity operator. This completes the proof.

For example, consider the Hermitian operators $\mathbf{Q}$ and $\mathbf{P}$ defined by $(\mathbf{Q}\psi)(\mathbf{x}) = \mathbf{x}\,\psi(\mathbf{x})$ and $(\mathbf{P}\psi)(\mathbf{x}) = -i\,\nabla\psi(\mathbf{x})$ on the space L^2 of functions $\psi(\mathbf{x}) = \psi(x_1, x_2, x_3)$. The set of six operators $\mathbf{Q} = (Q_1, Q_2, Q_3)$ and $\mathbf{P} = (P_1, P_2, P_3)$ is irreducible. A bounded operator which commutes with the operators $\mathbf{Q}$ is a function of $\mathbf{Q}$, because the set of three operators $\mathbf{Q}$ is a complete set of commuting operators. A function of $\mathbf{Q}$ which commutes with the operators $\mathbf{P}$ is a multiple of the identity operator.

20. VON NEUMANN ALGEBRAS, FUNCTIONS OF NONCOMMUTING OPERATORS

Suppose we are given a set of noncommuting Hermitian operators, for example $\mathbf{Q}$ and $\mathbf{P}$. Which bounded operators should be considered functions of the given operators? To answer this, we need the following.

Definition. A set of bounded operators is a *symmetric ring* or *symmetric algebra* or **algebra* if for any operators A and B in the set and any complex number c the operators cA, $A + B$, AB, and $A^\dagger$ also are in the set.

For example, the set of all bounded operators is a symmetric ring, as is the set of all complex multiples of the identity operator. A more interesting example of a symmetric ring of operators is the set of all bounded functions of a set of commuting Hermitian operators.

Consider again the question: Which bounded operators should be considered functions of a given set of noncommuting Hermitian operators? We want to include all operators which we can get by taking scalar multiples, sums, and products, starting with bounded functions of each Hermitian operator. This generates a symmetric ring of bounded operators, each of which is a polynomial of the bounded functions of the individual Hermitian operators.

[4] This step is valid for a closed unbounded operator A; see Riesz and Nagy, Sections 115–117.

We also want to include every operator which is a limit of these polynomials, just as for functions of commuting Hermitian operators. We are guided by the following.

Theorem 20.1.   A bounded operator B is a function of commuting Hermitian operators $A_1, A_2, \ldots, A_N$ if and only if B commutes with every bounded operator that commutes with $A_1, A_2, \ldots, A_N$.[5]

Definitions.   A bounded operator B is a *weak limit* of a set of bounded operators if for each choice of positive number ϵ, positive integer n, and vectors $\psi_1, \psi_2, \ldots, \psi_n$ and $\phi_1, \phi_2, \ldots, \phi_n$ there is an operator A in the set such that

$$|(\phi_k, A\psi_k) - (\phi_k, B\psi_k)| < \epsilon$$

for $k = 1, 2, \ldots, n$. The extension of a set of bounded operators to its weak limits is its *weak closure*. A set of bounded operators is *weakly closed* if it contains its weak limits. A symmetric ring of bounded operators which is weakly closed is a *von Neumann algebra* or *W* algebra*.

Theorem 20.1 describes a characteristic property of the bounded operators which are functions of given commuting Hermitian operators. The same property characterizes the bounded operators which we get by taking weak limits of our polynomials for functions of given noncommuting Hermitian operators. This is stated more precisely in the following.

Theorem 20.2.   Consider the set of all bounded operators which commute with every bounded operator which commutes with a given set of Hermitian operators. This is a von Neumann algebra. It is the weak closure of the symmetric ring of polynomials generated by taking scalar multiples, sums, and products, starting with bounded functions of each of the given Hermitian operators.[6]

We refer to the von Neumann algebra described in the last theorem as the von Neumann algebra generated by the given set of Hermitian operators. This is the set of all bounded operators which can be considered functions of the given Hermitian operators.

Theorem 20.1 shows that the von Neumann algebra generated by commuting Hermitian operators is the set of all bounded functions of these operators in the sense defined previously.

If a bounded operator is a function of a given set of Hermitian operators, then it should commute with every bounded operator which commutes with the given Hermitian operators, so it should be in the von Neumann algebra

---

[5] Riesz and Nagy, Sections 126, 129, and 130.
[6] Naimark, Section 34.

generated by the given Hermitian operators. Thus we can be certain that we have included every bounded operator which is a function of the given Hermitian operators.

On the other hand, if an operator is in the von Neumann algebra generated by a given set of Hermitian operators, then it can be gotten by taking scalar multiples, sums, products, and weak limits, starting with bounded functions of each of the given Hermitian operators. In this sense it is a function of the given Hermitian operators.

From Schur's lemma we see that the von Neumann algebra generated by an irreducible set of Hermitian operators is the set of all bounded operators. The only bounded operators which commute with an irreducible set of Hermitian operators are multiples of the identity operator, and all bounded operators commute with multiples of the identity operator. For example, the von Neumann algebra generated by Q and P is the set of all bounded operators on the space L^2 of functions $\psi(x)$.

See *Exercises and Applications* 6 and 9.

5

STATES

A mechanical description of a physical system generally requires three different kinds of ingredients. First, there are variables or measurable quantities characteristic of the system being studied; second, there are states which describe values of the variables at given times; third, there are equations of motion which determine how the values of the variables change in time.

21. MEASURABLE QUANTITIES

In classical mechanics the measurable quantities characteristic of a physical system are real or complex variables. In quantum mechanics they are represented by linear operators on a complex separable Hilbert space. There are many similarities. Hermitian operators are the analogs of real variables; non-Hermitian operators are the analogs of complex variables. A bounded non-Hermitian operator B can be written[1]

$$B = \operatorname{Re} B + i \operatorname{Im} B$$

in terms of bounded Hermitian operators $\operatorname{Re} B$ and $\operatorname{Im} B$, just as a complex variable is expressed in terms of real and imaginary parts. A bounded Hermitian operator is positive if and only if it is the square of a bounded Hermitian operator.[2] We assume that real quantities are represented by Hermitian operators and that non-negative real quantities are represented by positive Hermitian operators.

In classical mechanics if a set of real variables is measured, then any real or complex function of these variables also is measured. Functions of a

---

[1] See Section 9, *Adjoints, Hermitian Operators.*
[2] See Section 15, *Functions of an Operator, Stone's Theorem.*

set of commuting Hermitian operators have all the algebraic properties of functions of a set of real variables. We assume that if a set of quantities is represented by a set of commuting Hermitian operators, then a real or complex function of these quantities is represented by the same function of the operators.

The big difference is that multiplication of operators is not commutative. Functions of noncommuting Hermitian operators are more complicated than functions of real variables. We will see that if two quantities are represented by Hermitian operators which do not commute, then these quantities are not simultaneously measurable. Thus we have no basis in quantum mechanics for the classical concept of a function of these quantities.

22. DENSITY MATRICES AND TRACES

To describe states in quantum mechanics it is useful to know the following.

Definition. A *density matrix* is a positive self-adjoint operator W such that if the set of vectors ψ_k is an orthonormal basis, then

$$\sum_k (\psi_k, W\psi_k) = 1.$$

Theorem 22.1. If W is a density matrix, then W has a pure point spectrum, which means that

$$W = \sum_k w_k |\phi_k\rangle\langle\phi_k|,$$

where ϕ_k are orthonormal vectors and w_k are positive numbers such that $\sum_k w_k = 1$.[3]

The numbers w_k are eigenvalues of W, but they are not necessarily all different. The vectors ϕ_k are eigenvectors of W, but they are determined by W only to within a choice of an orthonormal basis in the eigenvector subspace for each different eigenvalue. The spectrum of W consists of the different numbers w_k and perhaps zero. Evidently W is bounded.

Theorem 22.2. Let W be a density matrix and B a bounded operator. If the set of vectors ϕ_k is an orthonormal basis and the set of vectors ψ_j is any other orthonormal basis, then

$$\sum_k (\phi_k, WB\phi_k), \quad \sum_j (\psi_j, WB\psi_j), \quad \sum_k (\phi_k, BW\phi_k), \quad \text{and} \quad \sum_j (\psi_j, BW\psi_j)$$

are finite, in fact the series are absolutely convergent, and they are all equal.

[3] See J. von Neumann, *Mathematical Foundations of Quantum Mechanics* (Princeton University Press, Princeton, New Jersey, 1955), pp. 188–191.

Proof. We can choose the vectors ϕ_k so that $W\phi_k = w_k\phi_k$ with $w_k \geq 0$ and $\sum_k w_k = 1$. The series

$$\sum_k \sum_j (W\phi_k, \psi_j)(\psi_j, B\phi_k) = \sum_k \sum_j w_k(\phi_k, \psi_j)(\psi_j, B\phi_k)$$

is absolutely convergent, because

$$|(\phi_k, \psi_j)(\psi_j, B\phi_k)| < |(\phi_k, \psi_j)|^2 + |(\psi_j, B\phi_k)|^2$$

and

$$\sum_k \sum_j w_k(|(\phi_k, \psi_j)|^2 + |(\psi_j, B\phi_k)|^2) = \sum_k w_k(\|\phi_k\|^2 + \|B\phi_k\|^2)$$
$$\leq \sum_k w_k(1 + \|B\|^2) = 1 + \|B\|^2.$$

Therefore changing the order of summation is all right, and

$$\sum_k (\phi_k, WB\phi_k) = \sum_k (W\phi_k, B\phi_k) = \sum_k \sum_j (W\phi_k, \psi_j)(\psi_j, B\phi_k)$$
$$= \sum_j \sum_k (B^\dagger\psi_j, \phi_k)(\phi_k, W\psi_j)$$
$$= \sum_j (B^\dagger\psi_j, W\psi_j) = \sum_j (\psi_j, BW\psi_j).$$

The absolute convergence of the double series implies the absolute convergence of both single series. Similarly we can show that

$$\sum_k (\phi_k, BW\phi_k) = \sum_j (\psi_j, WB\psi_j)$$

and establish the absolute convergence of both series. Finally, we have

$$\sum_k (\phi_k, WB\phi_k) = \sum_k w_k(\phi_k, B\phi_k) = \sum_k (\phi_k, BW\phi_k).$$

This completes the proof of the theorem.

We write

$$\text{Tr } WB = \sum_j (\psi_j, WB\psi_j)$$

and

$$\text{Tr } BW = \sum_j (\psi_j, BW\psi_j)$$

and call these the *trace* of WB or BW. The theorem tells us that these are independent of the choice of orthonormal basis vectors ψ_j and that

$$\text{Tr } WB = \text{Tr } BW.$$

For $B = 1$ we have $\text{Tr } W = 1$. This and the requirement that W is self-adjoint and positive are the properties which define a density matrix. Indeed, from the proof of the theorem we can see that a positive self-adjoint operator

W is a density matrix if it has an orthonormal basis of eigenvectors ϕ_k and

$$\sum_k (\phi_k, W\phi_k) = 1.$$

In terms of an orthonormal basis of eigenvectors ϕ_k of W we have

$$\text{Tr } WB = \sum_k w_k(\phi_k, B\phi_k),$$

where the w_k are positive numbers such that $\sum_k w_k = 1$. If B is self-adjoint, then Tr WB is real. If B is self-adjoint and positive, then Tr WB is real and non-negative. For any complex number c

$$\text{Tr } WcB = c \text{ Tr } WB.$$

For any bounded operators A and B

$$\text{Tr } W(A + B) = \text{Tr } WA + \text{Tr } WB.$$

Let $E_1, E_2, \ldots, E_k, \ldots$ be mutually orthogonal projection operators. Then $\sum_k E_k$ is a projection operator. For each k let $\psi_s^{\,k}$ be orthonormal basis vectors for the subspace onto which E_k projects. Then $E_j\psi_s^{\,k} = \delta_{jk}\psi_s^{\,k}$ and

$$\text{Tr } W \sum_j E_j = \sum_k \sum_s (\psi_s^{\,k}, W \sum_j E_j\psi_s^{\,k}) = \sum_k \sum_s (\psi_s^{\,k}, WE_k\psi_s^{\,k}) = \sum_k \text{Tr } WE_k.$$

23. REPRESENTATION OF STATES

A state describes values of measurable quantities. In quantum mechanics this description consists of probabilities. We can find probabilities for values of a quantity if we know the mean or expectation value for sufficiently many functions of that quantity. We assume that a state specifies a finite expectation value $\langle B \rangle$ for each bounded operator B. We assume that expectation values have the following properties.

(i) If B is self-adjoint, then $\langle B \rangle$ is real.

(ii) If B is self-adjoint and positive, then $\langle B \rangle$ is non-negative.

(iii) For any complex number c

$$\langle cB \rangle = c\langle B \rangle.$$

(iv) $$\langle A + B \rangle = \langle A \rangle + \langle B \rangle.$$

(v) $$\langle 1 \rangle = 1.$$

(vi) If $E_1, E_2, \ldots, E_k, \ldots$ are mutually orthogonal projection operators, then

$$\left\langle \sum_k E_k \right\rangle = \sum_k \langle E_k \rangle.$$

Properties (i) and (ii) correspond to the assumption that real quantities are represented by self-adjoint operators and non-negative real quantities by positive self-adjoint operators. If B represents a measurable quantity, then property (iii) corresponds to the assumption that cB represents c times that quantity. If A and B represent simultaneously measurable quantities, then property (iv) corresponds to the assumption that $A + B$ represents the sum of these quantities. Property (v) is a normalization. We can think of the identity operator as representing the trivial quantity whose value is always one. Property (vi) is a hypothesis of continuity; it extends the linearity of the expectation value to these infinite sums.[4]

From the preceding section we see that for each density matrix W, an expectation value with properties (i)–(vi) is defined by

$$\langle B \rangle = \mathrm{Tr}\ WB$$

for all bounded operators B. The generality of this form of expectation value is established by the following.

Theorem 23.1. If a finite expectation value $\langle B \rangle$ with properties (i)–(vi) is defined for all bounded operators B, then there is a unique density matrix W such that

$$\langle B \rangle = \mathrm{Tr}\ WB$$

for all bounded operators B.[5]

Discussion in lieu of a proof. For each vector ϕ of length one

$$\langle |\phi\rangle\langle\phi| \rangle = \mathrm{Tr}\ W\,|\phi\rangle\langle\phi| = (\phi, W\phi).$$

From these expectation values we can find $(\phi, W\phi)$ for all vectors ϕ, and using

$$(\psi + \chi, W[\psi + \chi]) = (\psi, W\psi) + (\chi, W\chi) + (\psi, W\chi) + (\chi, W\psi)$$

and

$$(\psi + i\chi, W[\psi + i\chi]) = (\psi, W\psi) + (\chi, W\chi) + i(\psi, W\chi) - i(\chi, W\psi)$$

we can solve for $(\psi, W\chi)$ for all vectors ψ and χ. Thus W is unique. Because $|\phi\rangle\langle\phi|$ is Hermitian, its expectation value is real, so $(\phi, W\phi)$ is real for all vectors ϕ. Therefore

$$(\psi, W\chi) + (\chi, W\psi) = [(\psi, W\chi) + (\chi, W\psi)]^* = (W\psi, \chi) + (W\chi, \psi)$$

[4] This hypothesis seems reasonable for most systems, but its general applicability has been questioned; for example, see G. Emch, *J. Math. Phys.* **7**, 1413 (1966).
[5] von Neumann, Chapter IV, Section 2; J. Dixmier, *Les algebres d'operateurs dans l'espace Hilbertien* (Gauthiers-Villars, Paris, 1957), Theorem 1, p. 54, and Exercise 9, p. 65; J. Langerholc, *J. Math. Phys.* **6**, 1210 (1965).

and

$$i(\psi, W\chi) - i(\chi, W\psi) = [i(\psi, W\chi) - i(\chi, W\psi)]^* = i(W\psi, \chi) - i(W\chi, \psi),$$

so $(\psi, W\chi) = (W\psi, \chi)$ for all vectors ψ and χ. Thus W is Hermitian. Because $|\phi\rangle\langle\phi|$ is positive, its expectation value is non-negative, so $(\phi, W\phi)$ is non-negative for all vectors ϕ. Thus W is positive. Because

$$\text{Tr } W = \langle 1 \rangle = 1,$$

W is a density matrix.

The theorem is easy to prove if the space is finite-dimensional. Then every operator is bounded. The set of all linear operators is a linear space with sums and scalar multiples of operators defined in the usual way. It is an easy exercise to check that an inner product is defined by

$$(A, B) = \text{Tr } A^\dagger B$$

for all operators A and B. Properties (iii) and (iv) state that the expectation value is a linear functional on the linear space of operators. This implies that there is an operator W such that

$$\langle A \rangle = (W, A) = \text{Tr } W^\dagger A$$

for all operators A. The proof is completed by the above demonstrations that W is unique and is a density matrix. For an infinite-dimensional space the proof cannot be done this way, because $\text{Tr } A^\dagger B$ does not converge for all bounded operators A and B. To do more would not be very instructive, so this is the end of our discussion.

We assume that every bounded Hermitian operator represents a measurable quantity.[6] Then each state is represented by a unique density matrix W. If W is a projection operator onto a one-dimensional subspace spanned by a vector ϕ of length one,

$$W = |\phi\rangle\langle\phi|,$$

then

$$\langle A \rangle = \text{Tr } WA = (\phi, A\phi)$$

for all bounded operators A. Thus the state represented by W is represented equally well by ϕ. The state determines ϕ only up to a phase factor; if b is a real number, then $e^{ib}\phi$ represents the same state as ϕ because

$$(e^{ib}\phi, Ae^{ib}\phi) = (\phi, A\phi)$$

for all bounded operators A.

---

[6] This assumption is relaxed in Section 28, *Superselection Rules*.

In general we have

$$W = \sum_k w_k \, |\phi_k\rangle\langle\phi_k|,$$

with orthonormal vectors ϕ_k and positive numbers w_k such that $\sum_k w_k = 1$. We can think of this as representing a statistical mixture of the states represented by the vectors ϕ_k; the probability is w_k that we have the state represented by ϕ_k. Indeed, for any bounded operator A

$$\langle A \rangle = \mathrm{Tr}\ WA = \sum_k w_k(\phi_k, A\phi_k).$$

This is just the average, weighted with the probabilities w_k, of the expectation values for the states represented by the vectors ϕ_k. Thus, in studying probabilities we can concentrate on states represented by vectors. If we know the probabilities for a value of a measurable quantity for the states represented by the vectors ϕ_k, then we can find the probability for this value for the state represented by W by calculating the average weighted with the probabilities w_k.

24. PROBABILITIES

Consider a state represented by a vector ψ, with $\|\psi\| = 1$, and consider a real measurable quantity represented by a self-adjoint operator A with spectral decomposition

$$A = \int_{-\infty}^{\infty} x\, dE_x.$$

We assume that a function f of this quantity is represented by the operator $f(A)$. If $f(A)$ is bounded, it has a finite expectation value

$$\langle f(A) \rangle = \big(\psi, f(A)\psi\big) = \int_{-\infty}^{\infty} f(x)\, d(\psi, E_x\psi) = \int_{-\infty}^{\infty} f(x)\, d\,\|E_x\psi\|^2.$$

By considering sufficiently many functions f, we can see that the possible values for the quantity represented by A are distributed over the spectrum of A with probability

$$\|E_x\psi\|^2 = (\psi, E_x\psi) = \langle E_x \rangle$$

that the value is $\leq x$. Indeed $\|E_x\psi\|^2$ is a monotonically increasing function of x, which converges to zero as $x \to -\infty$ and to one as $x \to +\infty$, and $\langle f(A) \rangle$ is the mean of $f(x)$ with respect to this probability distribution. For example, A^n represents the nth power of the quantity represented by A. If A is bounded, then A^n is bounded, and we have finite expectation values

$$\langle A^n \rangle = \int_{-\infty}^{\infty} x^n\, d\,\|E_x\psi\|^2$$

for $n = 0, 1, 2, \ldots$. These are the moments of the probability distribution. If A is unbounded, we can use these equations to define expectation values for the unbounded operators A^n in terms of the probabilities, but we have to look elsewhere to deduce the probabilities from expectation values of bounded operators. We can always use the unitary operators e^{itA}. As a function of all real t, their expectation values

$$\langle e^{itA} \rangle = \int_{-\infty}^{\infty} e^{itx} \, d \, \|E_x \psi\|^2$$

are the characteristic function of the probability distribution. This is always sufficient to determine the probability distribution.[7] The moments may be infinite, but the probability distribution and the characteristic function are always finite.

Suppose ψ is an eigenvector of A with eigenvalue a. Then

$$\langle A \rangle = (\psi, A\psi) = (\psi, a\psi) = a \, \|\psi\|^2 = a$$

and

$$\langle A^2 \rangle = (\psi, A^2\psi) = (\psi, a^2\psi) = a^2 \, \|\psi\|^2 = a^2,$$

so

$$\langle (A - \langle A \rangle)^2 \rangle = \langle A^2 \rangle - \langle A \rangle^2 = 0.$$

There is zero probability that the quantity represented by A has any value other than a. Indeed $E_x\psi = 0$ for $x < a$, and $E_x\psi = \psi$ for $x \geq a$ (Theorem 14.3), so $\|E_x\psi\|^2$ is zero for $x < a$ and one for $x \geq a$. The probability is zero that the value is $< a$, and the probability is one that the value is $\leq a$. Therefore the probability is one that the value is a. Conversely, suppose the probability is one that the quantity represented by A has the value a. Then the probabilities $\|E_x\psi\|^2$ are those just described. This implies (Theorem 14.3) that ψ is an eigenvector of A with eigenvalue a. We can check this very easily. If $\langle A \rangle = a$ and $\langle A^2 \rangle = a^2$, then a is real and

$$\|(A - a)\psi\|^2 = (\psi, (A - a)^2\psi) = \langle A^2 \rangle - \langle A \rangle^2 = 0,$$

so

$$A\psi = a\psi.$$

Suppose A has a pure point spectrum so that

$$A = \sum_k a_k I_k,$$

where the a_k are different eigenvalues of A and I_k is the projection operator onto the eigenvector subspace for a_k. The eigenvalues a_k are the possible values for the quantity represented by A. If ψ is an eigenvector of A with

---

[7] See W. Feller, *An Introduction to Probability Theory and Its Applications*, Volume II (John Wiley and Sons, New York, 1966), Chapters V and XV.

eigenvalue a_k, then the probability is one that the value is a_k. In general when ψ is not an eigenvector of A, the probability that the value is $\leq x$ is

$$\langle E_x \rangle = \sum_{a_k \leq x} \langle I_k \rangle,$$

so the probability that the value is a_k is

$$\langle I_k \rangle = (\psi, I_k \psi) = \|I_k \psi\|^2.$$

Indeed

$$0 \leq \|I_k \psi\|^2 \leq \|\psi\|^2 = 1$$

$$\sum_k (\psi, I_k \psi) = (\psi, \psi) = 1,$$

and for any function f

$$\langle f(A) \rangle = \sum_k f(a_k) \langle I_k \rangle.$$

Suppose A has a continuous spectrum. Let y be a point in the continuous spectrum which is not also in the point spectrum. Then y is not an eigenvalue, so there is no state for which the probability is one that the value of the quantity represented by A is y. But for any positive ϵ there are states for which the probability is one that the value is in the interval between $y - \epsilon$ and $y + \epsilon$. The projection operator $E_{y+\epsilon} - E_{y-\epsilon}$ is not zero, so there are vectors ψ, with $\|\psi\| = 1$, such that

$$(E_{y+\epsilon} - E_{y-\epsilon})\psi = \psi.$$

Then for $x \leq y - \epsilon$

$$E_x \psi = (E_x E_{y+\epsilon} - E_x E_{y-\epsilon})\psi = (E_x - E_x)\psi = 0,$$

and for $x \geq y + \epsilon$

$$E_x \psi = (E_x E_{y+\epsilon} - E_x E_{y-\epsilon})\psi = (E_{y+\epsilon} - E_{y-\epsilon})\psi = \psi,$$

so $\|E_x \psi\|^2$ is zero for $x \leq y - \epsilon$ and one for $x \geq y + \epsilon$. The probability is zero that the value is $\leq y - \epsilon$, and the probability is one that the value is $\leq y + \epsilon$. Therefore the probability is one that the value is between $y - \epsilon$ and $y + \epsilon$.

Similarly, we can find the joint probability distribution for two or more quantities represented by Hermitian operators which commute with each other. Consider again a state represented by a vector ψ, with $\|\psi\| = 1$, and consider two measurable quantities represented by commuting self-adjoint operators A_1 and A_2 with spectral decompositions

$$A_r = \int_{-\infty}^{\infty} x \, dE_x^{(r)}$$

for $r = 1, 2$. We assume that a function f of these quantities is represented by the operator $f(A_1, A_2)$. If $f(A_1, A_2)$ is bounded, it has a finite expectation value

$$\langle f(A_1, A_2) \rangle = (\psi, f(A_1, A_2)\psi) = \int_{-\infty}^{\infty} \int_{-\infty}^{\infty} f(x, y) \, d_x \, d_y(\psi, E_x^{(1)} E_y^{(2)}\psi)$$

$$= \int_{-\infty}^{\infty} \int_{-\infty}^{\infty} f(x, y) \, d_x \, d_y \, \| E_x^{(1)} E_y^{(2)}\psi \|^2.$$

By considering sufficiently many functions f, we can see that the probability is

$$\| E_x^{(1)} E_y^{(2)}\psi \|^2 = (\psi, E_x^{(1)} E_y^{(2)}\psi) = \langle E_x^{(1)} E_y^{(2)} \rangle$$

that the value of the quantity represented by A_1 is $\leq x$ and the value of the quantity represented by A_2 is $\leq y$. Indeed $\| E_x^{(1)} E_y^{(2)}\psi \|^2$ is a monotonically increasing function of either x or y, which converges to zero as x or $y \to -\infty$ and to one as x and $y \to +\infty$, and $\langle f(A_1, A_2) \rangle$ is the mean of $f(x, y)$ for this probability distribution. For example, the probability distribution may be determined by the moments $\langle A_1{}^m A_2{}^n \rangle$ for $m, n = 0, 1, 2, \ldots$ or by the characteristic function $\langle e^{i(tA_1 + uA_2)} \rangle$ for all real t and u.

Suppose $a_j^{(1)}$ is an eigenvalue of A_1 and $a_k^{(2)}$ is an eigenvalue of A_2. Let $I_j^{(1)}$ be the projection operator onto the subspace spanned by the eigenvectors of A_1 for $a_j^{(1)}$, and let $I_k^{(2)}$ be the projection operator onto the subspace spanned by the eigenvectors of A_2 for $a_k^{(2)}$. The probability is

$$\| I_j^{(1)} I_k^{(2)}\psi \|^2 = (\psi, I_j^{(1)} I_k^{(2)}\psi) = \langle I_j^{(1)} I_k^{(2)} \rangle$$

that the quantities represented by A_1 and A_2 have values $a_j^{(1)}$ and $a_k^{(2)}$. This probability is one if and only if ψ is an eigenvector of A_1 and A_2 with eigenvalues $a_j^{(1)}$ and $a_k^{(2)}$.

We see that probabilities are expectation values for projection operators. These are the only expectation values really needed to describe a state. That they are sufficient to determine the representation of a state is shown by the following.

Theorem 24.1. Consider operators on a separable Hilbert space of dimension larger than two. If for each projection operator E there is a non-negative real number $\langle E \rangle$ such that $\langle 1 \rangle = 1$ and

$$\left\langle \sum_k E_k \right\rangle = \sum_k \langle E_k \rangle$$

for every set of mutually orthogonal projection operators E_k, then there is a unique density matrix W such that

$$\langle E \rangle = \text{Tr } WE$$

for every projection operator E.[8]

[8] A. M. Gleason, *J. Math. Mech.* **6**, 885 (1957).

This requires fewer assumptions than Theorem 23.1. In particular it assumes nothing about the expectation value for quantities that are not simultaneously measurable.

25. PROBABILITIES FOR COMPLETE SETS OF COMMUTING OPERATORS

Consider a set of quantities represented by a complete set of commuting Hermitian operators $A_1, A_2, \ldots, A_N$ with pure point spectra.[9] Suppose that for a particular state the probability is one that the set of values of these quantities is a particular set of eigenvalues $a_j^{(1)}, a_k^{(2)}, \ldots, a_l^{(N)}$. Then the state is represented by an eigenvector $|a_j^{(1)}, a_k^{(2)}, \ldots, a_l^{(N)}\rangle$ of $A_1, A_2, \ldots, A_N$ for these eigenvalues. The state is completely determined, because for each set of eigenvalues there is not more than one linearly independent eigenvector. For any state represented by a vector ψ the probability that the values are $a_j^{(1)}, a_k^{(2)}, \ldots, a_l^{(N)}$ is

$$\langle|a_j^{(1)}, a_k^{(2)}, \ldots, a_l^{(N)}\rangle\langle a_j^{(1)}, a_k^{(2)}, \ldots, a_l^{(N)}|\rangle = |\langle a_j^{(1)}, a_k^{(2)}, \ldots, a_l^{(N)} \mid \psi\rangle|^2.$$

Thus the spectral representation describes the probabilities for the different possible sets of values.

We can think of $|\langle a_j^{(1)}, a_k^{(2)}, \ldots, a_l^{(N)} \mid \psi\rangle|^2$ as the probability of finding the state represented by $|a_j^{(1)}, a_k^{(2)}, \ldots, a_l^{(N)}\rangle$ given the state represented by ψ. Different states represented by different eigenvectors $|a_j^{(1)}, a_k^{(2)}, \ldots, a_l^{(N)}\rangle$ are independent in the sense that given one of them, the probability of finding another is zero. The orthonormal basis of eigenvectors $|a_j^{(1)}, a_k^{(2)}, \ldots, a_l^{(N)}\rangle$ represents a maximal set of independent states; given any other state, there are non-zero probabilities for finding states represented by eigenvectors $|a_j^{(1)}, a_k^{(2)}, \ldots, a_l^{(N)}\rangle$. Probabilities for the different possible sets of values for a complete set of commuting operators are probabilities for a maximal set of independent possibilities.

Given a vector ϕ of length one, we can choose an orthonormal basis such that ϕ is one of the basis vectors. Given an orthonormal basis of vectors ϕ_k, we can find a complete set of commuting bounded Hermitian operators with pure point spectra such that the vectors ϕ_k are eigenvectors of the complete set of commuting operators. Thus, if we assume that every bounded Hermitian operator represents a measurable quantity, we can assume that every vector ϕ of length one represents a state which is determined by values of quantities represented by commuting operators. For any vectors ϕ and ψ of length one we can think of $|(\phi, \psi)|^2$ as the probability of finding the state represented by ϕ given the state represented by ψ.

---

[9] See Section 17.

For complete sets of commuting operators with continuous spectra we consider the examples for which we have developed the spectral representation. The space L^2 of functions $\psi(\mathbf{x}) = \psi(x_1, x_2, x_3)$ can be used to describe a particle. The position is represented by the complete set of commuting operators $\mathbf{Q} = (Q_1, Q_2, Q_3)$ defined by $(Q\psi)(\mathbf{x}) = \mathbf{x}\,\psi(\mathbf{x})$. Recall[10] that the projection operators $E_x^{(r)}$ in the spectral decomposition of Q_r are defined by $(E_x^{(r)}\psi)(\mathbf{y}) = \psi(\mathbf{y})$ for $y_r \leq x$ and $(E_x^{(r)}\psi)(\mathbf{y}) = 0$ for $y_r > x$. For a state represented by a vector ψ of length one the probability that the components of the position are $\leq x, y, z$ is

$$\langle E_x^{(1)} E_y^{(2)} E_z^{(3)} \rangle = \int \psi(u, v, w)^* (E_x^{(1)} E_y^{(2)} E_z^{(3)} \psi)(u, v, w)\, du\, dv\, dw$$

$$= \int_{-\infty}^{x} du \int_{-\infty}^{y} dv \int_{-\infty}^{z} dw\, |\psi(u, v, w)|^2.$$

Therefore the probability that the position is in an infinitesimal volume $dx\, dy\, dz$ at the point (x, y, z) is

$$|\psi(x, y, z)|^2\, dx\, dy\, dz.$$

It is easy to check that this gives the correct expectation value

$$\int f(\mathbf{x})\, |\psi(\mathbf{x})|^2\, d\mathbf{x} = (\psi, f(\mathbf{Q})\psi)$$

for every bounded operator $f(\mathbf{Q})$. We can bring out the analogy with the case of point spectra by writing

$$|\langle x, y, z \mid \psi \rangle|^2 = |\psi(x, y, z)|^2$$

for the probability density function.

The momentum divided by $\hbar$ is represented by the complete set of commuting operators $\mathbf{P} = (P_1, P_2, P_3)$ defined by

$$(\mathbf{P}\psi)(\mathbf{x}) = -i\,\nabla\psi(\mathbf{x}).$$

For convenience we assume that we are working in a system of units for which $\hbar = 1$; then $\mathbf{P}$ represents the momentum. Recall[11] that the projection operators in the spectral decomposition of P_r are $F^{-1}E_x^{(r)}F$, where F is the unitary operator defined by the Fourier transform and $E_x^{(r)}$ are the projection operators in the spectral decomposition of Q_r. For a state represented by a

[10] Sections 14, 16, and 17.
[11] Section 18.

vector ψ of length one the probability that the components of the momentum are $\leq k_1, k_2, k_3$ is

$$\langle F^{-1}E^{(1)}_{k_1}FF^{-1}E^{(2)}_{k_2}FF^{-1}E^{(3)}_{k_3}F\rangle = (F\psi, E^{(1)}_{k_1}E^{(2)}_{k_2}E^{(3)}_{k_3}F\psi)$$
$$= \int_{-\infty}^{k_1}du\int_{-\infty}^{k_2}dv\int_{-\infty}^{k_3}dw\,|(F\psi)(u, v, w)|^2.$$

Therefore the probability density function for the momentum is

$$|\langle k_1, k_2, k_3\,|\,\psi\rangle|^2 = |(F\psi)(k_1, k_2, k_3)|^2.$$

We can check that this gives the correct expectation value

$$\int f(\mathbf{k})\,|(F\psi)(\mathbf{k})|^2\,dk = (F\psi, Ff(\mathbf{P})\psi) = (\psi, f(\mathbf{P})\psi)$$

for every bounded operator $f(\mathbf{P})$.

26.   UNCERTAINTY PRINCIPLE

Consider a quantity represented by a Hermitian operator A. For each state its *uncertainty* ΔA is defined by

$$(\Delta A)^2 = \langle A^2\rangle - \langle A\rangle^2 = \langle(A - \langle A\rangle)^2\rangle.$$

Evidently ΔA is non-negative and is zero if and only if the probability is zero that the quantity represented by A has any value other than $\langle A\rangle$.

Theorem 26.1.   Let A and B be Hermitian operators. For any state

$$(\Delta A)(\Delta B) \geq \tfrac{1}{2}\,|\langle AB - BA\rangle|.$$

Proof.   Let the state be represented by the density matrix

$$W = \sum_k w_k\,|\phi_k\rangle\langle\phi_k|.$$

For each k both $(\phi_k, [AB + BA]\phi_k)$ and $(\phi_k, -i[AB - BA]\phi_k)$ are real, because both $AB + BA$ and $-i[AB - BA]$ are Hermitian, so

$$(\phi_k, A^2\phi_k)(\phi_k, B^2\phi_k) = \|A\phi_k\|^2\,\|B\phi_k\|^2 \geq |(A\phi_k, B\phi_k)|^2 = |(\phi_k, AB\phi_k)|^2$$
$$= \left|\tfrac{1}{2}(\phi_k, [AB + BA]\phi_k) + \frac{i}{2}(\phi_k, -i[AB - BA]\phi_k)\right|^2$$
$$\geq |\tfrac{1}{2}(\phi_k, [AB - BA]\phi_k)|^2.$$

Replacing A and B by $A - \langle A\rangle$ and $B - \langle B\rangle$, we get

$$(\phi_k, [A - \langle A\rangle]^2\phi_k)(\phi_k, [B - \langle B\rangle]^2\phi_k) \geq |\tfrac{1}{2}(\phi_k, [AB - BA]\phi_k)|^2$$

for each k. If we consider $w_k^{\frac{1}{2}}(\phi_k, [A - \langle A \rangle]^2 \phi_k)^{\frac{1}{2}}$ and $w_k^{\frac{1}{2}}(\phi_k, [B - \langle B \rangle]^2 \phi_k)^{\frac{1}{2}}$ as the components of two vectors in l^2 and apply Schwarz's inequality, we get

$$\sum_j w_j(\phi_j, [A - \langle A \rangle]^2 \phi_j) \sum_k w_k(\phi_k, [B - \langle B \rangle]^2 \phi_k)$$

$$\geq \left| \sum_k w_k(\phi_k, [A - \langle A \rangle]^2 \phi_k)^{1/2}(\phi_k, [B - \langle B \rangle]^2 \phi_k)^{1/2} \right|^2$$

$$\geq \left| \tfrac{1}{2} \sum_k w_k(\phi_k, [AB - BA]\phi_k) \right|^2$$

or

$$(\Delta A)^2(\Delta B)^2 \geq |\tfrac{1}{2}\langle AB - BA \rangle|^2.$$

This completes the proof of the theorem.

The most interesting application is to the operators **Q** and **P** for which probability distributions were described in the preceding section. If we use the commutation relations

$$Q_r P_r - P_r Q_r = i,$$

we get the uncertainty relations

$$(\Delta Q_r)(\Delta P_r) \geq \tfrac{1}{2}$$

for $r = 1, 2, 3$. But Q_r and P_r are unbounded operators, so a rigorous derivation of the uncertainty relations should take account of domains.[12] Thus we will reconstruct the proof for this particular case and be careful to see that everything is properly defined.

We consider a pair of operators Q_r and P_r and a state represented by a density matrix

$$W = \sum_k w_k |\phi_k\rangle\langle\phi_k|.$$

We assume that $\langle Q_r \rangle$ and $\langle P_r \rangle$ are finite. This is necessary for the definition of ΔQ_r and ΔP_r. Neither ΔQ_r nor ΔP_r can be zero, because neither Q_r nor P_r has any eigenvalues and eigenvectors. Thus if either ΔQ_r or ΔP_r is infinite, the uncertainty relation is satisfied. Suppose ΔQ_r and ΔP_r are finite. This means that

$$\langle Q_r^2 \rangle = \sum_k w_k \int x_r^2 |\phi_k(\mathbf{x})|^2 \, d\mathbf{x}$$

and

$$\langle P_r^2 \rangle = \sum_j w_j \int k_r^2 |(F\phi_j)(\mathbf{k})|^2 \, d\mathbf{k}$$

---

[12] That this is necessary is shown by the failure of these uncertainty relations for angular coordinates and angular momenta which appear to have the same commutation relations.

are finite. This implies that each vector ϕ_k is in the domain of Q_r and in the domain of P_r. Therefore enough vectors are defined to get

$$\|(Q_r - \langle Q_r \rangle)\phi_k\|^2 \, \|(P_r - \langle P_r \rangle)\phi_k\|^2 \geq |([Q_r - \langle Q_r \rangle]\phi_k, [P_r - \langle P_r \rangle]\phi_k)|^2$$
$$\geq |\mathrm{Im}\,([Q_r - \langle Q_r \rangle]\phi_k, [P_r - \langle P_r \rangle]\phi_k)|^2$$

for each k. Integrating by parts, we can calculate

$$\mathrm{Im}\,([Q_r - \langle Q_r \rangle]\phi_k, [P_r - \langle P_r \rangle]\phi_k)$$

$$= -\left(\frac{i}{2}\right)\int [x_r - \langle Q_r \rangle]\phi_k(\mathbf{x})^*\left[-i\left(\frac{\partial}{\partial x_r}\right) - \langle P_r \rangle\right]\phi_k(\mathbf{x})\,d\mathbf{x}$$

$$+ \left(\frac{i}{2}\right)\int [x_r - \langle Q_r \rangle]\phi_k(\mathbf{x})\left[i\left(\frac{\partial}{\partial x_r}\right) - \langle P_r \rangle\right]\phi_k(\mathbf{x})^*\,d\mathbf{x}$$

$$= -\tfrac{1}{2}\int [x_r - \langle Q_r \rangle]\left(\frac{\partial}{\partial x_r}\right)\phi_k(\mathbf{x})^*\,\phi_k(\mathbf{x})\,d\mathbf{x}$$

$$= \tfrac{1}{2}\int \phi_k(\mathbf{x})^*\,\phi_k(\mathbf{x})\,d\mathbf{x} = \tfrac{1}{2},$$

because $x_r\phi_k(\mathbf{x})^*\phi_k(\mathbf{x})$ vanishes at infinite x_r because $x_r{}^2\,|\phi_k(\mathbf{x})|^2$ is integrable. Thus we have

$$\|(Q_r - \langle Q_r \rangle)\phi_k\|^2 \, \|(P_r - \langle P_r \rangle)\phi_k\|^2 \geq (\tfrac{1}{2})^2$$

for each k. We also have

$$(\Delta Q_r)^2 = \sum_k w_k \int (x_r - \langle Q_r \rangle)^2\,|\phi_k(\mathbf{x})|^2\,d\mathbf{x}$$

$$= \sum_k w_k\,\|(Q_r - \langle Q_r \rangle)\phi_k\|^2$$

and

$$(\Delta P_r)^2 = \sum_j w_j \int (k_r - \langle P_r \rangle)^2\,|(F\phi_j)(\mathbf{k})|^2\,d\mathbf{k}$$

$$= \sum_j w_j\,\|(P_r - \langle P_r \rangle)\phi_j\|^2.$$

If we consider $w_k^{1/2}\,\|(Q_r - \langle Q_r \rangle)\phi_k\|$ and $w_j^{1/2}\,\|(P_r - \langle P_r \rangle)\phi_j\|$ as the components of two vectors in l^2 and apply Schwarz's inequality, we get

$$(\Delta Q_r)^2(\Delta P_r)^2 \geq \left|\sum_k w_k\,\|(Q_r - \langle Q_r \rangle)\phi_k\|\,\|(P_r - \langle P_r \rangle)\phi_k\|\right|^2$$

$$\geq \left|\sum_k w_k(\tfrac{1}{2})\right|^2 = (\tfrac{1}{2})^2.$$

27. SIMULTANEOUS MEASURABILITY

The uncertainty relations set a limit on the precision with which values for Q_r and P_r can be specified by any one state. We interpret this as implying that position and momentum are not simultaneously measurable with unlimited precision. The following is a more direct argument that real quantities which are simultaneously measurable with unlimited precision are represented by commuting Hermitian operators.[13]

Let A_1 and A_2 be Hermitian operators with spectral decompositions

$$A_r = \int_{-\infty}^{\infty} x \, dE_x^{(r)}$$

for $r = 1, 2$. Suppose A_1 and A_2 represent quantities which are simultaneously measurable with unlimited precision. Then for any real numbers x and y measurements can determine if the values of the quantities represented by A_1 and A_2 are either

$$\leq x \quad \text{and} \quad \leq y,$$

or

$$\leq x \quad \text{and} \quad > y,$$

or

$$> x \quad \text{and} \quad \leq y,$$

or

$$> x \quad \text{and} \quad > y.$$

We can think of a real measurable quantity with values $1, 2, 3, 4$ corresponding respectively to these four mutually exclusive possibilities. This quantity is represented by an operator

$$I_1 + 2I_2 + 3I_3 + 4I_4,$$

where I_1, I_2, I_3, I_4 are mutually orthogonal projection operators such that

$$I_1 + I_2 + I_3 + I_4 = 1.$$

For a state represented by a vector ψ of length one the probability that the values of the quantities represented by A_1 and A_2 are $\leq x$ and $\leq y$ is $\|I_1\psi\|^2$. The probability is

$$\|(1 - E_x^{(1)})\psi\|^2 = 1 - \|E_x^{(1)}\psi\|^2$$

that the value of the quantity represented by A_1 is $> x$. If ϕ is a vector such that $I_1\phi$ is not zero, then

$$\psi = \left(\frac{1}{\|I_1\phi\|}\right) I_1\phi$$

---

[13] For a slightly different argument to the same end see von Neumann, Chapter III, Section 3.

represents a state for which the probability is

$$\|I_1\psi\|^2 = \|\psi\|^2 = 1$$

that the quantities represented by A_1 and A_2 have values $\leq x$ and $\leq y$. Therefore the probability is zero that the value of the quantity represented by A_1 is $> x$. This implies that

$$\|(1 - E_x^{(1)})I_1\phi\|^2 = 0.$$

Thus we have

$$(1 - E_x^{(1)})I_1 = 0.$$

In the same way we can conclude that

$$(1 - E_y^{(2)})I_1 = 0$$

$$(1 - E_x^{(1)})I_2 = 0 = E_y^{(2)}I_2$$

$$E_x^{(1)}I_3 = 0 = (1 - E_y^{(2)})I_3$$

$$E_x^{(1)}I_4 = 0 = E_y^{(2)}I_4.$$

It follows that

$$E_x^{(1)}E_y^{(2)} = E_x^{(1)}E_y^{(2)}I_1 + E_x^{(1)}E_y^{(2)}I_2 + E_x^{(1)}E_y^{(2)}I_3 + E_x^{(1)}E_y^{(2)}I_4$$

$$= E_x^{(1)}I_1 + E_x^{(1)}I_3 = I_1$$

and, similarly, that

$$E_y^{(2)}E_x^{(1)} = I_1.$$

Therefore $E_x^{(1)}$ and $E_y^{(2)}$ commute for all x and y. This implies that A_1 and A_2 commute. Thus real quantities which are simultaneously measurable with unlimited precision are represented by commuting Hermitian operators.

Consider a complete set of commuting Hermitian operators $A_1, A_2, \ldots, A_N$. Suppose B is a Hermitian operator such that the quantities represented by $A_1, A_2, \ldots, A_N$ and B are simultaneously measurable with unlimited precision. Then B commutes with $A_1, A_2, \ldots, A_N$. Therefore B is a function of $A_1, A_2, \ldots, A_N$. If the quantities represented by $A_1, A_2, \ldots, A_N$ are measured, the simultaneous measurement of the quantity represented by B gives no additional information.

These arguments are intended to justify our considering only joint probability distributions for commuting Hermitian operators. In particular we see that a joint probability distribution for a complete set of commuting Hermitian operators is a probability distribution over the different possible results of a maximal set of measurements.

Consider a bounded non-Hermitian operator

$$B = \operatorname{Re} B + i \operatorname{Im} B.$$

For each state we have separate probability distributions for the Hermitian operators Re B and Im B, and we have an expectation value

$$\langle B \rangle = \langle \text{Re } B \rangle + i \langle \text{Im } B \rangle.$$

But we have a joint probability distribution for Re B and Im B only if Re B and Im B commute. This is the case when Re B and Im B represent real quantities which are simultaneously measurable with unlimited precision. Then B represents a complex quantity whose real and imaginary parts are represented by Re B and Im B, so B represents a complex quantity which is measurable with unlimited precision. Evidently Re B and Im B commute if and only if B and $B^\dagger$ commute. Operators with this property are called *normal*. Hermitian and unitary operators are normal, as are complex functions of commuting Hermitian operators.

28. SUPERSELECTION RULES

We have assumed that every bounded Hermitian operator represents a measurable quantity. This assumption is acceptable for many simple physical systems, but there are systems for which it is wrong.

For example, suppose the description of a system admits rotations. Consider the operator $e^{-i2\pi J_3}$, which represents a rotation through an angle 2π about the z axis.[14] A measurable quantity is not changed by this rotation. Let B be a bounded operator which represents a measurable quantity. Then

$$e^{i2\pi J_3} B e^{-i2\pi J_3} = B.$$

But $e^{-i2\pi J_3}$ can have eigenvalues 1 and -1, because an eigenvalue of J_3 can be an integer or half an odd integer. If ψ is a vector such that $e^{-i2\pi J_3}\psi = \psi$, and ϕ is a vector such that $e^{-i2\pi J_3}\phi = -\phi$, then

$$(\phi, B\psi) = (\phi, e^{i2\pi J_3} B e^{-i2\pi J_3}\psi) = (e^{-i2\pi J_3}\phi, B e^{-i2\pi J_3}\psi) = -(\phi, B\psi),$$

so $(\phi, B\psi) = 0$. Suppose the system is such that J_3 does have both integral and half-odd-integral eigenvalues. Then every operator which represents a measurable quantity is reduced by the two subspaces corresponding to the eigenvalues 1 and -1 of $e^{-i2\pi J_3}$.

A restriction of the operators which represent measurable quantities is called a *superselection rule*. If a bounded operator, such as $e^{-i2\pi J_3}$, commutes with every Hermitian operator which represents a measurable quantity, but

[14] See Chapter VII, *Representation of Space-Time Transformations*. Properites of the angular momentum operators **J** are developed further in E. Merzbacher, *Quantum Mechanics* (John Wiley and Sons, New York, 1961), Chapter 15, Section 9.

is not a multiple of the identity operator, then we call it a *superselection operator*.

Consider the von Neumann algebra generated by the Hermitian operators which represent measurable quantities. This is the set of all bounded operators which can be considered functions of the Hermitian operators which represent measurable quantities.[15] We assume that every Hermitian operator in this von Neumann algebra represents a measurable quantity. Our only reason for not assuming that a bounded Hermitian operator represents a measurable quantity is that it fails to commute with a superselection operator. But every operator in the von Neumann algebra commutes with every superselection operator; an operator in the von Neumann algebra commutes with every bounded operator which commutes with the Hermitian operators which represent measurable quantities, and a superselection operator commutes with the Hermitian operators which represent measurable quantities.

Let $B = \operatorname{Re} B + i \operatorname{Im} B$ be an operator in the von Neumann algebra generated by the Hermitian operators which represent measurable quantities. Then the Hermitian operators $\operatorname{Re} B$ and $\operatorname{Im} B$ are in the von Neumann algebra and represent measurable quantities. Thus we assume that a state specifies a finite expectation value

$$\langle B \rangle = \langle \operatorname{Re} B \rangle + i \langle \operatorname{Im} B \rangle.$$

We assume that these expectation values for operators in the von Neumann algebra have the properties (i)–(vi) which we previously assumed for all bounded operators.[16] Then the representation of states by density matrices is established by the following.

Theorem 28.1.   If a finite expectation value $\langle B \rangle$ with properties (i)–(vi) is defined for all operators B in the von Neumann algebra generated by the Hermitian operators which represent measurable quantities, then there is a density matrix W such that

$$\langle B \rangle = \operatorname{Tr} WB$$

for all operators B in the von Neumann algebra.

Discussion of where a proof can be found.   Dixmier[17] shows that there are vectors ϕ_k of length one and positive numbers w_k such that

$$\langle B \rangle = \sum_k w_k (\phi_k, B \phi_k).$$

---

[15] See Section 20, *von Neumann Algebras, Functions of Noncommuting Operators*.
[16] See Section 23, *Representation of States*.
[17] Dixmier, Theorem 1, p. 54, and Exercise 9, p. 65.

It follows that

$$\sum_k w_k = \sum_k w_k(\phi_k, \phi_k) = \langle 1 \rangle = 1.$$

An operator W is defined by

$$W\psi = \sum_k w_k(\phi_k, \psi)\phi_k$$

for every vector ψ, because

$$\left\| \sum_{k=m+1}^{n} w_k(\phi_k, \psi)\phi_k \right\| \le \sum_{k=m+1}^{n} w_k \|\psi\| \to 0$$

as $m, n \to \infty$. For all vectors ψ and ϕ

$$(\phi, W\psi) = \sum_k w_k(\phi_k, \psi)(\phi, \phi_k) = (W\phi, \psi).$$

Therefore W is bounded and Hermitian.[18] By letting $\psi = \phi$ in the last equation, we see that W is positive. If the set of vectors ψ_j is an orthonormal basis, then[19]

$$\sum_k w_k(\phi_k, B\phi_k) = \sum_k \sum_j w_k(B^\dagger \phi_k, \psi_j)(\psi_j, \phi_k)$$
$$= \sum_j \sum_k w_k(\phi_k, B\psi_j)(\psi_j, \phi_k) = \sum_j (\psi_j, WB\psi_j).$$

Thus $\langle B \rangle = \operatorname{Tr} WB$. In particular $\operatorname{Tr} W = \langle 1 \rangle = 1$, so W is a density matrix. Thus Dixmier's proof is complete.

When there is a superselection rule, the density matrix which represents a state is not always unique.

Suppose there is a complete set of commuting Hermitian operators which represent measurable quantities. Every superselection operator commutes with these operators and therefore is a function of them. Therefore all superselection operators commute with each other. It follows that they can be simultaneously diagonalized.[20] We assume that this does not require a continuous decomposition. Then we have mutually orthogonal projection operators I_k, with $\sum_k I_k = 1$, such that every superselection operator has the diagonal form $\sum_k c_k I_k$ with eigenvalues c_k, and each I_k is labeled by eigenvalues of superselection operators: if $k \ne k'$, then there is a superselection operator $\sum_j c_j I_j$ such that $c_k \ne c_{k'}$. This is the usual structure of superselection operators.

[18] See Theorem 11.1.
[19] Absolute convergence of the double series is proved as in Theorem 22.2, so changing the order of summation is all right.
[20] See J. M. Jauch, *Helv. Phys. Acta* **33**, 711 (1960).

Let B be an operator in the von Neumann algebra generated by the Hermitian operators which represent measurable quantities. If $\sum_j c_j I_j$ is a superselection operator, then

$$B \sum_j c_j I_j = \sum_j c_j I_j B.$$

Multiplying on the left by $I_{k'}$ and on the right by I_k, we get

$$c_k I_{k'} B I_k = c_{k'} I_{k'} B I_k.$$

Therefore $I_{k'} B I_k = 0$ for $k' \neq k$. Then B commutes with each projection operator I_k, because B is reduced by the subspace onto which I_k projects.

On the other hand, if B is a bounded operator which commutes with each projection operator I_k, then B commutes with every superselection operator. In other words B commutes with every bounded operator which commutes with the Hermitian operators which represent measurable quantities. This means that B is in the von Neumann algebra generated by the Hermitian operators which represent measurable quantities. Thus the von Neumann algebra is just the set of all bounded operators which commute with the projection operators I_k.

If W is a density matrix, then $\sum_k I_k W I_k$ is a density matrix. If B is a bounded operator which commutes with each projection operator I_k, then

$$\text{Tr } WB = \text{Tr } \sum_k I_k W B I_k = \text{Tr } \sum_k I_k W I_k B.$$

Thus W and $\sum_k I_k W I_k$ represent the same state. In particular a state represented by a vector ψ of length one is represented equally well by the density matrix

$$\sum_k I_k |\psi\rangle\langle\psi| I_k$$

or by a vector $\sum_k e^{ib_k} I_k \psi$ for any phase factors e^{ib_k}.

For example, consider the superselection operator $e^{-i2\pi J_3}$. Let ψ be a vector such that $e^{-i2\pi J_3}\psi = \psi$, and let ϕ be a vector such that $e^{-i2\pi J_3}\phi = -\phi$. Suppose $\|\psi + \phi\| = 1$. Then $\psi + \phi$ and

$$e^{-i2\pi J_3}(\psi + \phi) = \psi - \phi$$

represent the same state.

The density matrix $\sum_k I_k W I_k$ commutes with the projection operators I_k. For each state there is only one density matrix with this property. It is determined by expectation values for projection operators which commute with the projections I_k. Indeed, these probabilities for measurable quantities are sufficient to establish the representation of a state by a density matrix. This is shown by the following application of Gleason's theorem.[21]

---

[21] Theorem 24.1.

Theorem 28.2. Let each I_k project onto a subspace of dimension larger than two. If for each projection operator E which commutes with the projections I_k there is a non-negative real number $\langle E \rangle$ such that $\langle 1 \rangle = 1$ and

$$\left\langle \sum_j E_j \right\rangle = \sum_j \langle E_j \rangle$$

for every set of mutually orthogonal projection operators E_j which commute with the projections I_k, then there is a unique density matrix W which commutes with the projections I_k such that

$$\langle E \rangle = \operatorname{Tr} WE$$

for every projection operator E which commutes with the projections I_k.

Proof. We have $\langle EI_k \rangle$ for every projection operator E which commutes with I_k. Applying Gleason's theorem[21] to the subspace onto which I_k projects, we get a positive Hermitian operator W_k on this subspace such that

$$\langle EI_k \rangle = \operatorname{Tr} W_k EI_k$$

and

$$\operatorname{Tr} W_k I_k = \langle I_k \rangle \leq 1.$$

Let

$$W = \sum_k W_k I_k.$$

This is a positive Hermitian operator, and

$$\operatorname{Tr} W = \sum_k \operatorname{Tr} W_k I_k = \sum_k \langle I_k \rangle = \left\langle \sum_k I_k \right\rangle = \langle 1 \rangle = 1.$$

If E is a projection operator which commutes with the projections I_k, then

$$\langle E \rangle = \left\langle \sum_k EI_k \right\rangle = \sum_k \langle EI_k \rangle = \sum_k \operatorname{Tr} WEI_k = \operatorname{Tr} WE.$$

This density matrix W commutes with the projections I_k. Any density matrix W which commutes with the projections I_k is a sum

$$W = \sum_k I_k W = \sum_k I_k^2 W = \sum_k I_k W I_k$$

in which $I_k W I_k$ is determined by

$$\langle EI_k \rangle = \operatorname{Tr} WEI_k = \operatorname{Tr} WI_k E = \operatorname{Tr} I_k WI_k E$$

for projection operators E which commute with the projections I_k. This completes the proof.

See *Exercises and Applications* 5 and 7.

6

EQUATIONS OF MOTION

States describe values or probabilities for measurable quantities at given times. Equations of motion determine how these values or probabilities change in time. It is sufficient for a state to specify expectation values of measurable quantities; therefore it is sufficient for an equation of motion to specify how expectation values change in time. There are at least two ways to make expectation values depend on time. One is to work with states represented by vectors $\psi(t)$ which depend on the time t and let each measurable quantity be represented by an operator A which is independent of time. Then an expectation value has the time dependence

$$\langle A \rangle(t) = \big(\psi(t), A\psi(t)\big).$$

This is called the *Schrödinger picture*. Another way is to let each measurable quantity be represented by an operator $A(t)$ which depends on time and work with states represented by vectors ψ which are independent of time. Then an expectation value has the time dependence

$$\langle A(t) \rangle = \big(\psi, A(t)\psi\big).$$

This is called the *Heisenberg picture*. To begin we work in the Schrödinger picture; later we can transfer to the Heisenberg picture simply by requiring that the two pictures give the same time dependence for expectation values.

The most important feature of the Schrödinger picture is that the change of state vectors in time is a linear transformation. We need not assume this; we will derive it. A key step in this derivation is the application of Wigner's theorem for unitary and antiunitary operators described in the following section. This, and in fact all the mathematics developed in this chapter for the Schrödinger picture, is used again in the next chapter.

29. ANTIUNITARY OPERATORS

Our discussion of the Schrödinger picture is our first occasion to use anti-unitary antilinear operators. We use them again in the next chapter; in particular the time-reversal operator is antilinear and antiunitary.

For each vector ψ let $T\psi$ be a vector specified by T so that

$$T(\psi + \phi) = T\psi + T\phi$$

and

$$Tc\psi = c^*T\psi$$

for all vectors ψ and ϕ and complex numbers c. Then T is an *antilinear operator*.

We say that an antilinear operator T has an *inverse* T^{-1} if T^{-1} is an antilinear operator such that

$$T^{-1}T = 1 = TT^{-1}.$$

Theorem 29.1. For an antilinear operator T to have an inverse T^{-1} it is necessary and sufficient that for each vector ψ there is one and only one vector ϕ such that $\psi = T\phi$.

This is proved just as for a linear operator.[1] It shows that T^{-1} is unique and is necessarily antilinear.

We say that an antilinear operator T is *antiunitary* if it has an inverse T^{-1} and $\|T\psi\| = \|\psi\|$ for all vectors ψ.

Theorem 29.2. If T is an antiunitary antilinear operator, then

$$(T\phi, T\psi) = (\phi, \psi)^*$$

for all vectors ψ and ϕ.

The proof of this is similar to the proof that unitary operators preserve inner products.[2]

For example, $(T\psi)(\mathbf{x}) = \psi(\mathbf{x})^*$ defines an antiunitary antilinear operator T on the space L^2 of square-integrable functions $\psi(\mathbf{x})$.

If T is an antilinear operator, then T^2 is a linear operator; if T is antiunitary, then T^2 is unitary.

The role played by antiunitary antilinear operators in quantum mechanics is established by the following.

[1] See Theorem 7.1.
[2] See Theorem 8.1.

Theorem 29.3. Let ψ and ψ' be vectors of length one related by a correspondence which is defined and one-to-one up to phase factors for all vectors of unit length; for each vector ψ of length one the corresponding projection operator $|\psi'\rangle\langle\psi'|$ is specified, and for each vector ψ' of length one the corresponding projection operator $|\psi\rangle\langle\psi|$ is specified. If

$$|(\phi, \psi)| = |(\phi', \psi')|$$

for all vectors ψ and ϕ of length one, then there is an operator T, which is either linear and unitary or antilinear and antiunitary, such that the correspondence is described by

$$\psi' = T\psi$$

for all vectors ψ of length one.[3]

We continue to refer to a linear operator simply as an operator, with the understanding that if an operator is not described as antilinear then it is linear.

30. SCHRÖDINGER PICTURE

Suppose the state at time $t = 0$ is represented by a vector $\psi(0)$ and the state at another time t is represented by a vector $\psi(t)$. How are these vectors related? We assume that every vector $\psi(0)$ such that $\|\psi(0)\| = 1$ represents a possible state at time zero and every vector $\psi(t)$ such that $\|\psi(t)\| = 1$ represents a possible state at time t. We assume that every bounded Hermitian operator represents a measurable quantity.[4] Then the vector representing a state is determined up to a phase factor by the state. Thus we assume that $|\psi(t)\rangle\langle\psi(t)|$ is determined by $\psi(0)$ and that $|\psi(0)\rangle\langle\psi(0)|$ is determined by $\psi(t)$.

Let $\psi(0)$ and $\phi(0)$ represent two possible states at time zero, and let $\psi(t)$ and $\phi(t)$ represent the corresponding states at time t. Then $|(\phi(0), \psi(0))|^2$ is the probability of finding the state represented by $\phi(0)$, given the state represented by $\psi(0)$, at time zero, and $|(\phi(t), \psi(t))|^2$ is the probability of finding the state represented by $\phi(t)$, given the state represented by $\psi(t)$, at time t. These probabilities should be the same. Thus we assume that

$$|(\phi(0), \psi(0))|^2 = |(\phi(t), \psi(t))|^2.$$

[3] E. P. Wigner, *Group Theory* (Academic Press, New York, 1959), Appendix to Chapter 20 and first section of Chapter 26; V. Bargmann, *J. Math. Phys.* **5**, 862 (1964).
[4] This assumption is relaxed in Section 32, *Including Superselection Rules.*

From these assumptions and Theorem 29.3 it follows that there is an operator $T(t)$, which is either linear and unitary or antilinear and antiunitary, such that if $\psi(0)$ represents the state at time zero then $T(t)\psi(0)$ represents the state at time t. This determines $T(t)$ up to a phase factor. For suppose $U(t)$ is another unitary or antiunitary operator such that if $\psi(0)$ represents the state at time zero, then $U(t)\psi(0)$ represents the state at time t. Then

$$|U(t)\psi(0)\rangle\langle U(t)\psi(0)| = |T(t)\psi(0)\rangle\langle T(t)\psi(0)|$$

for every vector $\psi(0)$ such that $\|\psi(0)\| = 1$. Taking $\psi(0) = (1/\|\phi\|)\phi$, we see that $U(t)\phi$ and $T(t)\phi$ can differ only by a phase factor for each nonzero vector ϕ. This phase factor is independent of the vector ϕ. Suppose

$$U(t)\phi = e^{ia}T(t)\phi$$

and

$$U(t)\psi = e^{ib}T(t)\psi$$

with a and b real. We know that

$$U(t)(\phi + \psi) = U(t)\phi + U(t)\psi = e^{ia}T(t)\phi + e^{ib}T(t)\psi$$

can differ by at most a phase factor from

$$T(t)(\phi + \psi) = T(t)\phi + T(t)\psi.$$

If $T(t)\phi$ and $T(t)\psi$ are linearly independent, this implies that $e^{ia} = e^{ib}$. If $T(t)\phi$ and $T(t)\psi$ are linearly dependent, we can deduce that $e^{ia} = e^{ib}$ by making comparisons with a third vector which is linearly independent. Thus there is a phase factor $e^{ib(t)}$, with $b(t)$ real, such that

$$U(t) = e^{ib(t)}T(t).$$

We assume that if $\psi(t')$ represents the state at time t', then $T(t)\psi(t')$ represents the state at time $t' + t$. The way a state changes in time is invariant under translations in time; it is the same between times t' and $t' + t$ as between times zero and t. This should be true for closed systems, which are isolated from outside influences, or for systems influenced only by static external forces. A state can change differently at different times only if its evolution depends on what is happening outside the system, because the state itself is a maximal specification of information about the system.

If $\psi(0)$ represents the state at time zero, then $T(t')\psi(0)$ represents the state at time t', and both $T(t' + t)\psi(0)$ and $T(t)T(t')\psi(0)$ represent the state at time $t' + t$. Letting $\psi(0) = (1/\|\phi\|)\phi$, we see that $T(t + t')\phi$ and $T(t)T(t')\phi$ can differ only by a phase factor for each nonzero vector ϕ. That this phase factor is independent of the vector ϕ is established just as for $U(t)$ and $T(t)$

above. Thus there is a complex number $\omega(t, t')$, with $|\omega(t, t')| = 1$, such that

$$T(t + t') = \omega(t, t')T(t)T(t').$$

In particular

$$T(t) = \omega(t/2, t/2)\, T(t/2)T(t/2)$$

and $T(t/2)T(t/2)$ is linear and unitary regardless of whether $T(t/2)$ is linear and unitary or antilinear and antiunitary. Thus $T(t)$ is linear and unitary for all nonzero t. For $t = 0$ we can let $T(0) = 1$. It is remarkable that changes of state vectors in time are necessarily linear transformations; they preserve superpositions of states defined by linear combinations of vectors.

If ψ and ϕ are vectors of length one, then $|(\phi, T(t)\psi)|^2$ is the probability of finding the state represented by ϕ, given the state represented by $T(t)\psi$, at time t. We assume that this is a continuous function of t. It follows that $|(\phi, T(t)\psi)|^2$ is a continuous function of t for all vectors ψ and ϕ.

Theorem 30.1.   For each real t let $T(t)$ be a unitary operator. If $|(\phi, T(t)\psi)|^2$ is a continuous function of t for all vectors ψ and ϕ, if $T(0) = 1$, and if for all real t and t' there are complex numbers $\omega(t, t')$, with $|\omega(t, t')| = 1$, such that

$$T(t + t') = \omega(t, t')T(t)\, T(t'),$$

then there are unitary operators $U(t) = e^{ib(t)}T(t)$, with $b(t)$ real, such that $U(0) = 1$,

$$U(t + t') = U(t)U(t')$$

for all real t and t', and $(\phi, U(t)\psi)$ is a continuous function of t for all vectors ψ and ϕ.[5]

Thus we are rid of the phase factors $\omega(t, t')$.

Stone's theorem[6] states that there is a unique self-adjoint operator H such that

$$U(t) = e^{-itH}.$$

If $\psi(0)$ represents the state at time zero, then

$$\psi(t) = U(t)\psi(0) = e^{-itH}\psi(0)$$

represents the state at time t. If $\psi(t)$ is in the domain of H, then

$$i\left(\frac{d}{dt}\right)\psi(t) = H\psi(t).$$

This is the *Schrödinger equation* and H is the *Hamiltonian*.

---

[5] E. P. Wigner, *Ann. Math.* **40**, 149 (1939); V. Bargmann, *Ann. Math.* **59**, 1 (1954).
[6] Theorem 15.1.

The time dependence of states determines $U(t)$ up to a phase factor $e^{ib(t)}$ which is a continuous function of t such that $e^{ib(0)} = 1$ and

$$e^{ib(t+t')} = e^{ib(t)}e^{ib(t')}$$

for all real t and t'. The only possibility is $e^{ib(t)} = e^{ibt}$ with b a real number. Thus H is determined to within addition of a real number.

31. HEISENBERG PICTURE

In practice we are not given time-dependent state vectors $\psi(t)$ from which we can deduce the Hamiltonian H. We have to solve the Schrödinger equation for $\psi(t)$. But the Schrödinger equation has no content unless we know H. To get an idea how to guess H, we transfer to the Heisenberg picture.

Suppose a vector ψ of length one represents the state at time zero. In the Schrödinger picture the expectation value of a quantity represented by an operator A has the time dependence

$$\langle A\rangle(t) = (e^{-itH}\psi, Ae^{-itH}\psi) = (\psi, e^{itH}Ae^{-itH}\psi).$$

We assume that it has the same time dependence in the Heisenberg picture, where the state is represented by the same vector ψ at all times. Therefore the quantity represented by the operator $A = A(0)$ at time zero must be represented by the operator

$$A(t) = e^{itH}Ae^{-itH} = e^{itH}A(0)e^{-itH}$$

at time t.

Because this is a unitary transformation, it preserves general properties of operators. If $A(0)$ is bounded, then $A(t)$ is bounded. Suppose $A(0)$ is Hermitian. Then $A(t)$ is Hermitian. If $A(0)$ is positive, then $A(t)$ is positive. In fact $A(0)$ and $A(t)$ have the same spectrum. If the projection operators in the spectral decomposition of $A(0)$ are $E_x(0)$, then the projection operators in the spectral decomposition of $A(t)$ are

$$E_x(t) = e^{itH}E_x(0)e^{-itH}.$$

It is an easy exercise to check that the set of operators $E_x(t)$ is a spectral family of projection operators simply because e^{itH} is unitary and the set of operators $E_x(0)$ is a spectral family of projection operators. Then we just have to note that

$$(\phi, A(t)\psi) = (e^{-itH}\phi, A(0)e^{-itH}\psi)$$

$$= \int_{-\infty}^{\infty} x \, d(e^{-itH}\phi, E_x(0)e^{-itH}\psi)$$

$$= \int_{-\infty}^{\infty} x \, d(\phi, e^{itH}E_x(0)e^{-itH}\psi)$$

for all vectors ϕ and all vectors ψ in the domain of $A(t)$.

For a function f of $A(t)$ we have

$$(\phi, f(A(t))\psi) = \int_{-\infty}^{\infty} f(x) \, d(\phi, E_x(t)\psi)$$

$$= \int_{-\infty}^{\infty} f(x) \, d(e^{-itH}\phi, E_x(0)e^{-itH}\psi)$$

$$= (e^{-itH}\phi, f(A(0))e^{itH}\psi)$$

$$= (\phi, e^{itH}f(A(0))e^{-itH}\psi).$$

Therefore $f(A(t)) = e^{itH}f(A(0))e^{-itH}$.

If $A_1(0), A_2(0), \ldots, A_N(0)$ are mutually commuting Hermitian operators, then $A_1(t), A_2(t), \ldots, A_N(t)$ are mutually commuting Hermitian operators. Just as for a single operator, one finds that a function f of these operators has the time dependence

$$f(A_1(t), A_2(t), \ldots, A_N(t)) = e^{itH}f(A_1(0), A_2(0), \ldots, A_N(0))e^{-itH}.$$

If the set of operators $A_1(0), A_2(0), \ldots, A_N(0)$ is a complete set of commuting operators, then the set of operators $A_1(t), A_2(t), \ldots, A_N(t)$ also is a complete set of commuting operators; if B is a bounded operator which commutes with $A_1(t), A_2(t), \ldots, A_N(t)$, then $e^{-itH}Be^{itH}$ is a bounded operator which commutes with

$$e^{-itH}A_r(t)e^{itH} = A_r(0)$$

for all $r = 1, 2, \ldots, N$, so there is a function f such that

$$e^{-itH}Be^{itH} = f(A_1(0), A_2(0), \ldots, A_N(0))$$

and

$$B = e^{itH}f(A_1(0), A_2(0), \ldots, A_N(0))e^{-itH}$$

$$= f(A_1(t), A_2(t), \ldots, A_N(t)).$$

Algebraic relations between noncommuting operators also are preserved in time. If $A(0)$, $B(0)$, and $C(0)$ are operators such that

$$A(0) = B(0) + C(0),$$

then

$$A(t) = B(t) + C(t).$$

Similarly, if

$$A(0) = B(0)C(0),$$

then

$$A(t) = B(t)C(t).$$

The quantity represented by the Hamiltonian operator H is a constant of the motion, because

$$e^{itH} H e^{-itH} = H.$$

Consideration of simple systems which have analogs in classical mechanics suggests that $\hbar H$ represents the energy. For convenience we assume that we are working with a system of units for which $\hbar = 1$; then H represents the energy.

For example consider a single particle. Let the position and momentum at time zero be represented by the operators $\mathbf{Q}$ and $\mathbf{P}$ defined by

$$(\mathbf{Q}\psi)(\mathbf{x}) = \mathbf{x}\,\psi(\mathbf{x})$$

and

$$(\mathbf{P}\psi)(\mathbf{x}) = -i\nabla\psi(\mathbf{x})$$

on the space L^2 of functions $\psi(\mathbf{x})$. Then the position and momentum at time t are represented by

$$\mathbf{Q}(t) = e^{itH} \mathbf{Q} e^{-itH}$$

and

$$\mathbf{P}(t) = e^{itH} \mathbf{P} e^{-itH}.$$

The nonrelativistic energy for a particle of mass m in a static potential $V(\mathbf{x})$ is represented by the operator

$$H = \frac{1}{2m}\mathbf{P}^2 + V(\mathbf{Q}).$$

We assume that this is the Hamiltonian operator. Then the equations of motion for the position and momentum operators are

$$\frac{d}{dt}\mathbf{Q}(t) = -i[\mathbf{Q}(t)H - H\mathbf{Q}(t)] = -ie^{itH}[\mathbf{Q}H - H\mathbf{Q}]e^{-itH}$$

$$= \frac{1}{m}e^{itH}\mathbf{P}e^{-itH} = \frac{1}{m}\mathbf{P}(t)$$

and

$$\frac{d}{dt}\mathbf{P}(t) = -i[\mathbf{P}(t)H - H\mathbf{P}(t)] = -ie^{itH}[\mathbf{P}H - H\mathbf{P}]e^{-itH}$$

$$= -e^{itH}\nabla V(\mathbf{Q})e^{-itH} = -\nabla V(\mathbf{Q}(t)),$$

which are the same as Hamilton's equations in classical mechanics. Indeed we have Newton's equations

$$m \frac{d^2}{dt^2} \mathbf{Q}(t) = -\nabla V(\mathbf{Q}(t)).$$

If we choose a Hamiltonian operator which differs from this one by more than a real number, then we will get different equations of motion for $\mathbf{Q}(t)$ and $\mathbf{P}(t)$; on the space of functions $\psi(\mathbf{x})$ the only operators which commute with $\mathbf{Q}$ and $\mathbf{P}$ are multiples of the identity operator.

Thus a good guess for the operator which represents the energy is a good guess for the Hamiltonian operator.

For example, the energy of a particle in an oscillator potential is represented by the operator

$$H = \frac{1}{2m} \mathbf{P}^2 + \tfrac{1}{2} m \omega^2 \mathbf{Q}^2.$$

This Hamiltonian gives

$$\mathbf{Q}(t) = \mathbf{Q} \cos \omega t + \frac{1}{m\omega} \mathbf{P} \sin \omega t$$

and

$$\mathbf{P}(t) = \mathbf{P} \cos \omega t - m\omega \mathbf{Q} \sin \omega t$$

for the time-dependent position and momentum operators.

32. INCLUDING SUPERSELECTION RULES

In Section 30, *Schrödinger Picture*, we assumed that every bounded Hermitian operator represents a measurable quantity, so that a vector representing a state is determined up to a phase factor. If there are superselection rules, our discussion has to be refined.

Suppose we have superselection rules with the discrete structure discussed previously:[7] there are mutually orthogonal projection operators I_k, with $\sum_k I_k = 1$, such that the bounded Hermitian operators which represent measurable quantities are those which commute with the projections I_k. We refer to a subspace onto which an I_k projects as a *superselection subspace*.

Each state is represented by one density matrix which commutes with the projections I_k. We consider only density matrices with this property. Then we have a one-to-one correspondence between density matrices and states. Let W be a density matrix which commutes with the projections I_k.

[7] See Section 28, *Superselection Rules*.

If W is a projection $|\phi\rangle\langle\phi|$ onto the subspace spanned by a vector ϕ of length one, then ϕ is in a superselection subspace. In any case there are orthonormal vectors ϕ_j, each in a superselection subspace, such that

$$W = \sum_j w_j \, |\phi_j\rangle\langle\phi_j|$$

with positive numbers w_j such that $\sum_j w_j = 1$: if I is the projection onto the eigenvector subspace for an eigenvalue of W, then I commutes with I_k, so the operators II_k for different k are mutually orthogonal projections, and $I = \sum_k II_k$; for each k and each positive eigenvalue of W, we can choose any orthonormal basis vectors ϕ_j for the subspace onto which II_k projects.

Let W and W' be density matrices which represent an evolving state at time zero and time t. We assume that this defines a one-to-one correspondence for all density matrices which commute with the projections I_k. We need not assume that a density matrix which is a projection $|\phi\rangle\langle\phi|$ corresponds to a projection $|\phi'\rangle\langle\phi'|$ as we did in Section 30, *Schrödinger Picture*. We derive this from the following.

In $W = \sum_j w_j \, |\phi_j\rangle\langle\phi_j|$ each $|\phi_j\rangle\langle\phi_j|$ is a density matrix which commutes with the projections I_k, and w_j is the probability of finding the state represented by $|\phi_j\rangle\langle\phi_j|$ at time zero. We should have the same probability for finding the state represented by $|\phi_j\rangle\langle\phi_j|'$ at time t. The states represented by the density matrices $|\phi_j\rangle\langle\phi_j|$ at time zero are independent in the sense that given one of them there is no probability of finding another. The same should be true when these states are represented by the density matrices $|\phi_j\rangle\langle\phi_j|'$ at time t. For a bounded operator B which commutes with the projections I_k, the expectation value at time t should be the mean of the expectation values $\mathrm{Tr}\, |\phi_j\rangle\langle\phi_j|' \, B$ with probabilities w_j:

$$\sum_j w_j \, \mathrm{Tr}\, |\phi_j\rangle\langle\phi_j|'B.$$

Therefore we assume that $W' = \sum_j w_j \, |\phi_j\rangle\langle\phi_j|'$.

Suppose W is not a projection. Then there are different density matrices W_1 and W_2 which commute with the projections I_k such that $W = wW_1 + (1 - w)W_2$ and $W' = wW_1' + (1 - w)W_2'$ with $0 < w < 1$; for example, let wW_1 be one term of $\sum_j w_j|\phi_j\rangle\langle\phi_j|$ and let $(1 - w)W_2$ be the remainder. If W' were a projection $|\psi\rangle\langle\psi|$ onto the subspace spanned by a vector ψ of length one, we would have

$$w(\psi, W_1'\psi) + (1 - w)(\psi, W_2'\psi)$$
$$= w\, \mathrm{Tr}\, W_1'W' + (1 - w)\, \mathrm{Tr}\, W_2'W' = \mathrm{Tr}\, W'^2 = \mathrm{Tr}\, W' = 1,$$

from which it follows that $(\psi, W_1'\psi) = 1 = (\psi, W_2'\psi)$, which implies that $W_1' = |\psi\rangle\langle\psi| = W_2'$. But the different density matrices W_1 and W_2 cannot correspond to the same density matrix $W_1' = W_2'$. Therefore W' is not a projection. Thus we see that projections correspond to projections. Let ψ and ψ' be vectors of length one, each in a superselection subspace, such that $|\psi\rangle\langle\psi|' = |\psi'\rangle\langle\psi'|$. This defines a correspondence which is one-to-one up to phase factors for all vectors of length one in superselection subspaces. We may write $\psi(0)$ and $\psi(t)$ for corresponding vectors ψ and ψ'.

Motivated by consideration of probabilities, just as for no superselection rules,[8] we assume that

$$|(\phi, \psi)|^2 = |(\phi', \psi')|^2,$$

and that $|(\phi, \psi(t))|^2$ is a continuous function of t, for all vectors of length one in superselection subspaces. It follows that $\psi' = \psi(t)$ is in the same superselection subspace as $\psi = \psi(0)$. For each superselection subspace we have the same situation as for no superselection rules.

Consider the superselection subspace onto which I_k projects. Proceeding as for no superselection rules,[8] we get a self-adjoint operator H_k on this subspace such that if a vector ψ in this subspace represents the state at time zero, then $e^{-itH_k}\psi$ represents the state at time t. This determines H_k to within addition of a real number.

Let $U(t) = \sum_k e^{-itH_k} I_k$. This defines unitary operators which commute with the projections I_k such that $U(0) = 1$ and $U(t + t') = U(t)U(t')$ for all real t and t'. For any vectors ψ and ϕ

$$(\phi, U(t)\psi) = \sum_k (\phi, e^{-itH_k} I_k \psi)$$

is a continuous function of t, because each term of the series is continuous and the series converges uniformly in t. From Stone's theorem[9] we get a unique self-adjoint operator H which commutes with the projections I_k such that $U(t) = e^{-itH}$. If ψ is a vector in the superselection subspace onto which I_k projects, then

$$e^{-itH}\psi = e^{-itH_k}\psi.$$

If the state at time zero is represented by a density matrix

$$W = \sum_j w_j |\phi_j\rangle\langle\phi_j|$$

with orthonormal vectors ϕ_j, each in a superselection subspace, then the state at time t is represented by the density matrix

$$\sum_j w_j |e^{-itH}\phi_j\rangle\langle e^{-itH}\phi_j| = \sum_j w_j e^{-itH} |\phi_j\rangle\langle\phi_j| e^{itH} = e^{-itH}We^{itH}.$$

---

[8] See Section 30, *Schrödinger Picture.*
[9] Theorem 15.1.

Suppose K is another self-adjoint operator such that

$$e^{-itK} W e^{itK} = e^{-itH} W e^{itH}$$

for every such density matrix W. Then

$$e^{itH} e^{-itK} |\phi\rangle\langle\phi| = |\phi\rangle\langle\phi| e^{itH} e^{-itK}$$

for every vector ϕ of length one in a superselection subspace. It follows that $e^{itH} e^{-itK}$ commutes with the projections I_k, so $e^{itH} e^{-itK}$ is reduced by the superselection subspaces. On each superselection subspace $e^{itH} e^{-itK}$ must be a multiple of the identity operator, because for vectors ϕ of length one in the superselection subspace the projection operators $|\phi\rangle\langle\phi|$ are irreducible on the superselection subspace. Therefore $e^{-itK} = e^{-itH} e^{itH} e^{-itK}$ differs from e^{-itH} only by a phase factor on each superselection subspace. Thus H is determined to within addition of a different real number on each superselection subspace.

For a bounded operator B which commutes with the projections I_k the expectation value at time t is

$$\mathrm{Tr}\ e^{-itH} W e^{itH} B = \mathrm{Tr}\ W e^{itH} B e^{-itH},$$

if the state is represented by the density matrix W at time zero. We assume that it is the same in the Heisenberg picture where the state is represented by the same density matrix W at all times. Suppose B' is a bounded operator which commutes with the projections I_k such that

$$\mathrm{Tr}\ W B' = \mathrm{Tr}\ W e^{itH} B e^{-itH}$$

for every density matrix W which commutes with the projections I_k. Then B' is reduced by the superselection subspaces. On each superselection subspace, B' is determined by the expectation values

$$\mathrm{Tr}\ |\phi\rangle\langle\phi| B' = (\phi, B'\phi)$$

for vectors ϕ of length one in the superselection subspace. Therefore

$$B' = e^{itH} B e^{-itH}.$$

Thus the time dependence of operators in the Heisenberg picture is determined from the time dependence of density matrices in the Schrödinger picture.

For each t we have a one-to-one correspondence of operators B and B' in the von Neumann algebra generated by the Hermitian operators which represent measurable quantities. For any operators A and B in the von Neumann algebra and any complex number c we have

$$(A + B)' = A' + B', \qquad (cA)' = cA',$$
$$(AB)' = A'B', \quad \text{and} \quad (A^{\dagger})' = (A')^{\dagger}.$$

One can start with this as a postulate and prove that there are unitary operators $U(t)$ such that $B' = U(t)^{\dagger} B U(t)$ for all operators B in the von Neumann algebra. The advantage of this approach is that it is not necessary to assume that the von Neumann algebra has the discrete structure which we have used. But something more is needed to get unitary operators $U(t) = e^{-itH}$ which are in the von Neumann algebra so that H represents a measurable quantity. This can be done with an assumption which implies that the spectrum of H has a lower bound.[10]

[10] G. F. Dell'Antonio, *Commun. Math. Phys.* **2**, 384 (1966); R. V. Kadison and J. R. Ringrose, *Commun. Math. Phys.* **4**, 32 (1967).

7

REPRESENTATION OF SPACE-TIME TRANSFORMATIONS

The mathematics which we used to get equations of motion can be applied to other transformations in space and time. We consider the space-time transformations which characterize the relativity of Galileo and Newton. The Lorentz transformations of Einstein relativity can be handled in much the same way.

33. GALILEI GROUP, UNITARY REPRESENTATION AND GENERATORS

Let $\mathbf{x} \to R\mathbf{x}$ denote a rotation of vectors $\mathbf{x}$ in real three-dimensional space. A rotation is specified by three real parameters; for example, we can specify the axis of rotation and the angle of rotation. We consider also translations $\mathbf{x} \to \mathbf{x} + \mathbf{r}$ of vectors $\mathbf{x}$ in real three-dimensional space. Each translation is specified by a real three-vector $\mathbf{r}$. We combine these with transformations $\mathbf{x} \to \mathbf{x} + \mathbf{v}t$ of space-time coordinates $\mathbf{x}, t$. These are called *Galilei transformations*. Each is specified by a real three-vector $\mathbf{v}$. Finally we include time translations $t \to t + s$ specified by real numbers s. Putting all these together, we get transformations

$$\mathbf{x} \to R\mathbf{x} + \mathbf{r} + \mathbf{v}t$$

$$t \to t + s$$

of space-time coordinates $\mathbf{x}, t$.

Let τ_1 and τ_2 denote two of these transformations. The *product* $\tau_2\tau_1$ is the transformation gotten by doing first the transformation τ_1 and then the transformation τ_2. For example, each of these transformations is a product of a space rotation, a space translation, a Galilei transformation, and a time translation. With this product the set of all such transformations is a *group*. By this we mean the following.

(i) The product of any two of these transformations is a transformation of the same kind: if τ_1 is the transformation specified by R_1, $\mathbf{r}_1$, $\mathbf{v}_1$, and s_1, and if τ_2 is the transformation specified by R_2, $\mathbf{r}_2$, $\mathbf{v}_2$, and s_2, then $\tau_2\tau_1$ is the transformation specified by R_2R_1, $R_2\mathbf{r}_1 + \mathbf{v}_2 s_1 + \mathbf{r}_2$, $R_2\mathbf{v}_1 + \mathbf{v}_2$, and $s_1 + s_2$, where R_2R_1 denotes the product of the two rotations.

(ii) The product is associative: $\tau_3(\tau_2\tau_1) = (\tau_3\tau_2)\tau_1$ for any three transformations.

(iii) There is an *identity* transformation τ_0, namely $\mathbf{x} \to \mathbf{x}$ and $t \to t$, such that $\tau_0\tau = \tau = \tau\tau_0$ for every transformation τ.

(iv) For each transformation τ there is an *inverse* transformation τ^{-1} such that $\tau^{-1}\tau = \tau_0 = \tau\tau^{-1}$, where τ_0 is the identity transformation: if τ is the transformation specified by R, $\mathbf{r}$, $\mathbf{v}$, and s, then τ^{-1} is the transformation specified by R^{-1}, $R^{-1}\mathbf{v}s - R^{-1}\mathbf{r}$, $-R^{-1}\mathbf{v}$, and $-s$, where R^{-1} denotes the inverse rotation.

Each transformation is specified by ten real parameters. The parameters of a product transformation $\tau_2\tau_1$ are analytic functions of the parameters of τ_1 and τ_2 (provided suitable parameters are used for the rotations). Such a group is called a *ten-parameter Lie group*. This group is called the *Galilei group*.

A subset of transformations $\tau(u)$ depending on a real parameter u is called a *one-parameter subgroup* if $\tau(0)$ is the identity transformation and $\tau(u_1 + u_2) = \tau(u_1)\tau(u_2)$.[1] Rotations about a fixed axis form a one-parameter subgroup whose parameter is the angle of rotation. From three one-parameter subgroups of rotations about three orthogonal axes we can get every rotation by taking products. Space translations for $\mathbf{r}$ on a fixed axis form a one-parameter subgroup, as do Galilei transformations for $\mathbf{v}$ on a fixed axis. By taking products we can get every space translation and every Galilei transformation from the one-parameter subgroups of space translations and Galilei transformations for three orthogonal axes. Finally, the time translations form a one-parameter subgroup. Thus the Galilei group is a combination of ten one-parameter subgroups.

We consider quantum-mechanical descriptions of a physical system with respect to different space-time coordinates related by transformations of the Galilei group. We transform one of these descriptions to another by changing

[1] We always use "canonical coordinates," which means that we choose parameters such that this equation holds.

the state vectors and leaving the operators unchanged, as in the Schrödinger picture. The same transformations of expectation values can be gotten by changing the operators and leaving the state vectors unchanged, as in the Heisenberg picture.

Let ψ and ψ' be vectors which represent the same state described with respect to different space-time coordinates related by a transformation τ of the Galilei group. We assume that this defines a correspondence which is one-to-one up to phase factors for all vectors of unit length.[2] We assume that, given one state, the probability of finding another is the same in both descriptions, so that

$$|(\phi, \psi)|^2 = |(\phi', \psi')|^2$$

for all vectors of length one. Then Wigner's theorem[3] tells us that there is an operator $T(\tau)$, which is either linear and unitary or antilinear and antiunitary, such that the correspondence is described by

$$\psi' = T(\tau)\psi$$

for all vectors of length one. This determines $T(\tau)$ up to a phase factor.[4]

Suppose that after one transformation τ_1 of space-time coordinates, we do a second transformation τ_2. We assume that after the transformation $\psi \to T(\tau_1)\psi$ of state vectors, we can do the transformation

$$T(\tau_1)\psi \to T(\tau_2)T(\tau_1)\psi$$

to get state vectors with respect to the twice-transformed space-time coordinates. The way state vectors transform is invariant under transformations of space-time coordinates. This assumption is acceptable for closed systems which are isolated from outside influences. It implies that there are complex numbers $\omega(\tau_2, \tau_1)$, with $|\omega(\tau_2, \tau_1)| = 1$, such that

$$T(\tau_2\tau_1) = \omega(\tau_2, \tau_1)T(\tau_2)T(\tau_1)$$

for all transformations τ_1 and τ_2 of the Galilei group.[4]

For each one-parameter subgroup of transformations $\tau(u)$ we have

$$T(\tau(u)) = \omega(\tau(u/2), \tau(u/2))T(\tau(u/2))T(\tau(u/2)).$$

The square of a unitary linear or antiunitary antilinear operator is linear and unitary. Therefore $T(\tau(u))$ is linear and unitary. Every transformation τ of

---

[2] We assume that every bounded Hermitian operator represents a measurable quantity so that a vector representing a state is determined up to a phase factor. If there are superselection rules the discussion has to be refined as in Section 32, *Including Superselection Rules.*
[3] Theorem 29.3.
[4] See Section 30, *Schrödinger Picture.*

the Galilei group is a product of transformations from one-parameter subgroups, so every operator $T(\tau)$ is a product of unitary operators and phase factors. Therefore $T(\tau)$ is linear and unitary for every transformation τ of the Galilei group. With the product property described in the preceding paragraph, we have a *unitary representation up to phase factors* of the group.

Consider the one-parameter subgroup of transformations $\tau(u)$ for each of the following: rotations about the x, y, or z axis with $u = \theta_1$, θ_2, or θ_3 being the angle of rotation; space translations along the x, y, or z axis with $u = r_1$, r_2, or r_3; Galilei transformations along the x, y, or z axis with $u = v_1$, v_2, or v_3; time translations with $u = s$. If the state is represented by ψ with respect to given space-time coordinates, then $|(\phi, T(\tau(u))\psi)|^2$ is the probability of finding the state represented by ϕ with respect to the space-time coordinates produced by $\tau(u)$. We assume that this is a continuous function of u for all vectors ψ and ϕ of length one. For the identity transformation $\tau(0)$ we can let $T(\tau(0)) = 1$. For each one-parameter subgroup of rotations we take $T(\tau(\theta))$ to be defined for all real θ according to $\tau(\theta + 2\pi n) = \tau(\theta)$ for integers n. Then

$$T(\tau(\theta + \theta')) = \omega(\tau(\theta'), \tau(\theta))T(\tau(\theta'))T(\tau(\theta))$$

holds for all real θ and θ', and $|(\phi, T(\tau(\theta))\psi)|^2$ is continuous for all real θ if it is continuous for one complete circle of rotations. For each of these one-parameter subgroups of transformations $\tau(u)$ there are unitary operators $U(u)$, which differ only by phase factors from the operators $T(\tau(u))$, such that $U(0) = 1$,

$$U(u_1 + u_2) = U(u_1)U(u_2)$$

for all real u_1 and u_2, and $(\phi, U(u)\psi)$ is a continuous function of u for all vectors ψ and ϕ.[5] Stone's theorem[6] tells us that there is a self-adjoint operator A such that

$$U(u) = e^{iuA}$$

for all real u. We call A the *generator* for the one-parameter subgroup. It is determined to within addition of a real number by the transformations of state vectors.

This is all quite similar to our discussion of the Schrödinger picture in which each step was considered in more detail. Indeed, for time translations $\tau(s)$ we have

$$U(s) = e^{isH},$$

where H is the Hamiltonian. If the evolving state is represented by vectors $\psi(t)$ with respect to a time coordinate t, then with respect to $t' = t + s$, it is

---

[5] See Theorem 30.1.
[6] Theorem 15.1.

represented by

$$\psi'(t') = \psi(t) = \psi(t' - s) = e^{isH}\psi(t').$$

Let $\mathbf{P} = (P_1, P_2, P_3)$ denote the Hermitian operators which are generators for the one-parameter subgroups of space translations, and let $e^{-ir_1P_1}$, $e^{-ir_2P_2}$, and $e^{-ir_3P_3}$ be the unitary operators for space translations by distances r_1, r_2, and r_3 along the x, y, and z axes respectively. Let $\mathbf{J} = (J_1, J_2, J_3)$ denote the Hermitian operators which are generators for the one-parameter subgroups of rotations, and let $e^{-i\theta_1J_1}$, $e^{-i\theta_2J_2}$, and $e^{-i\theta_3J_3}$ be the unitary operators for rotations through angles θ_1, θ_2, and θ_3 about the x, y, and z axes respectively. Let $\mathbf{G} = (G_1, G_2, G_3)$ denote the Hermitian operators which are generators for the one-parameter subgroups of Galilei transformations, and let $e^{iv_1G_1}$, $e^{iv_2G_2}$, and $e^{iv_3G_3}$ be the unitary operators for Galilei transformations for velocities v_1, v_2, and v_3 along the x, y, and z axes respectively.

34. COMMUTATION RELATIONS

For the generators H, $\mathbf{P}$, $\mathbf{J}$, $\mathbf{G}$ we get commutation relations characteristic of the Galilei group from the requirement that products of unitary operators for different one-parameter subgroups correspond to the products of the space-time transformations in the Galilei group. To do this, we write the unitary operators as exponential power series in terms of the generators, which requires a few words of explanation.

Let A be a bounded self-adjoint operator and let E_x be the projection operators in its spectral decomposition. Then

$$e^{iuA}\psi = \sum_{k=0}^{\infty}\left(\frac{i^ku^k}{k!}\right)A^k\psi$$

for all real u and every vector ψ, because[7]

$$\left\| e^{iuA}\psi - \sum_{k=0}^{n}\left(\frac{i^ku^k}{k!}\right)A^k\psi \right\|^2 = \int_{-\infty}^{\infty}\left| e^{iux} - \sum_{k=0}^{n}\frac{i^ku^kx^k}{k!}\right|^2 d\|E_x\psi\|^2$$

converges to zero as $n \to \infty$. Indeed, the integral is over the spectrum of A, which is contained in a finite interval of x, and the power series for e^{iux} converges uniformly in a finite interval. Therefore the integral is smaller than the product of

$$\int_{-\infty}^{\infty} d\|E_x\psi\|^2 = \|\psi\|^2$$

[7] See Section 15, *Functions of an Operator, Stone's Theorem.*

and a number which converges to zero as $n \to \infty$. It follows that

$$\left\| e^{iuA} - \sum_{k=0}^{n} \left(\frac{i^k u^k}{k!} \right) A^k \right\| \to 0$$

as $n \to \infty$. With this kind of convergence we can use a double power series. Let A_1 and A_2 be bounded self-adjoint operators, and let

$$U_n = \sum_{k=0}^{n} \left(\frac{i^k u_1{}^k}{k!} \right) A_1{}^k$$

and

$$V_n = \sum_{k=0}^{n} \left(\frac{i^k u_2{}^k}{k!} \right) A_2{}^k$$

for real u_1 and u_2. Then

$$\| e^{iu_1 A_1} e^{iu_2 A_2} - U_m V_n \|$$

$$\leq \| e^{iu_1 A_1} e^{iu_2 A_2} - e^{iu_1 A_1} V_n \| + \| e^{iu_1 A_1} V_n - U_m V_n \|$$

$$\leq \| e^{iu_1 A_1} \| \, \| e^{iu_2 A_2} - V_n \| + \| e^{iu_1 A_1} - U_m \| \, \| V_n \|$$

$$\leq \| e^{iu_1 A_1} \| \, \| e^{iu_2 A_2} - V_n \| + \| e^{iu_1 A_1} - U_m \| \, (\| e^{iu_2 A_2} - V_n \| + \| e^{iu_2 A_2} \|)$$

which converges to zero as $m, n \to \infty$. It follows that

$$e^{iu_1 A_1} e^{iu_2 A_2} \psi = \sum_{j,k=0}^{\infty} \left(\frac{i^j u_1{}^j}{j!} \right) \left(\frac{i^k u_2{}^k}{k!} \right) A_1{}^j A_2{}^k \psi$$

for all real u_1 and u_2 and every vector ψ.

We want to use power series like this when the operators A are generators H, $\mathbf{P}$, $\mathbf{J}$, $\mathbf{G}$ of the Galilei group. These operators are generally all unbounded, so the individual terms of the power series are not even defined for all vectors ψ. But for a continuous unitary representation of a Lie group there is a dense set of vectors ψ, called *analytic vectors*, on which the power series can be used for all generators A and small values of the parameters u.[8]

Let A_j and A_k be two of the generators H, $\mathbf{P}$, $\mathbf{J}$, $\mathbf{G}$. We get

$$e^{i\epsilon A_k} e^{i\epsilon A_j} e^{-i\epsilon A_k} e^{-i\epsilon A_j} = 1 + \epsilon^2 (A_j A_k - A_k A_j) + \cdots$$

by taking power series to second order in ϵ. This is a product of four operators each of which represents a transformation of the Galilei group. Therefore it must be equal up to a phase factor to the operator

$$e^{isH} e^{iv_1 G_1} e^{iv_2 G_2} e^{iv_3 G_3} e^{-ir_1 P_1} e^{-ir_2 P_2} e^{-ir_3 P_3} e^{-i\theta_1 J_1} e^{-i\theta_2 J_2} e^{-i\theta_3 J_3}$$

for parameters which specify the transformation which is the product of the four transformations in the Galilei group. These parameters are analytic

[8] E. Nelson, *Ann. Math.* **70**, 572 (1959). As is partly evident from the following, our representations up to phase factors can be gotten from true representations of an eleven-parameter group; see V. Bargmann, *Ann. Math.* **59**, 1 (1954) and J. Voisin, *J. Math. Phys.* **6**, 1519 (1965).

functions of ϵ, which is the parameter of each of the four transformations. If ϵ is zero, then each of the four transformations is the identity transformation, so the product transformation is the identity transformation, and all of its parameters are zero. Therefore these parameters have power series in ϵ with no constant terms. Thus the lower-order terms in the series in powers of ϵ for this operator are the lower-order terms of

$$1 + i(sH + v_1 G_1 + v_2 G_2 + v_3 G_3 - r_1 P_1 - r_2 P_2 - r_3 P_3 - \theta_1 J_1 - \theta_2 J_2 - \theta_3 J_3).$$

By comparing, we see that the commutator

$$[A_j, A_k] = A_j A_k - A_k A_j$$

is a linear combination of generators, and perhaps the identity operator:

$$[A_j, A_k] = i \sum_{m=1}^{10} c_{jkm} A_m + i b_{jk},$$

where $A_1, A_2, \ldots, A_{10}$ are the generators H, $\mathbf{P}$, $\mathbf{J}$, $\mathbf{G}$ and b_{jk} is a real number. A multiple b_{jk} of the identity operator is included because the two operators we are comparing may differ by a phase factor. The c_{jkm} are real numbers which are called the *structure constants* of the group. We see that they are determined by group products for small values of the parameters. The converse also is true; the structure constants of a Lie group determine all group products for small values of the parameters.[9]

For example, the four operators in the product

$$e^{i\epsilon P_1} e^{i\epsilon G_1} e^{-i\epsilon P_1} e^{-i\epsilon G_1} = 1 + \epsilon^2 [G_1, P_1] + \cdots$$

represent a Galilei transformation, a space translation, and their inverses. The product of these four transformations is the identity transformation in the Galilei group, because Galilei transformations and space translations commute. Therefore the operator product must be equal up to a phase factor to the identity operator. It follows that

$$[G_1, P_1] = 0 + (\quad)1,$$

where $(\quad)1$ indicates a possible multiple of the identity operator. Similarly, we get

$$[G_j, P_k] = 0 + (\quad)1, \qquad [G_j, G_k] = 0 + (\quad)1, \qquad [P_j, P_k] = 0 + (\quad)1,$$
$$[P_j, H] = 0 + (\quad)1, \qquad [J_j, H] = 0 + (\quad)1$$

with possible multiples of the identity operator, for $j, k = 1, 2, 3$, because the corresponding transformations of the Galilei group commute. Also

$$[J_j, G_j] = 0 + (\quad)1, \qquad [J_j, P_j] = 0 + (\quad)1$$

[9] See, for example, L. Pontrjagin, *Topological Groups*, Second Edition, translated by A. Brown (Gordon and Breach, New York, 1966), Chapter 10.

with possible multiples of the identity operator, for $j = 1, 2, 3$, because rotations about an axis commute with Galilei transformations and space translations along the same axis.

The four operators in the product

$$e^{i\epsilon H}e^{i\epsilon G_1}e^{-i\epsilon H}e^{-i\epsilon G_1} = 1 + \epsilon^2[G_1, H] + \cdots$$

represent a Galilei transformation, a time translation, and their inverses. These transformations do not commute. Their product in the Galilei group is the transformation

$$(x_1, x_2, x_3, t) \rightarrow (x_1 - \epsilon t, x_2, x_3, t)$$
$$\rightarrow (x_1 - \epsilon t, x_2, x_3, t - \epsilon)$$
$$\rightarrow (x_1 - \epsilon t + \epsilon t - \epsilon^2, x_2, x_3, t - \epsilon)$$
$$\rightarrow (x_1 - \epsilon^2, x_2, x_3, t),$$

which is a space translation by $-\epsilon^2$ along the x axis. Therefore the operator product must be equal up to a phase factor to

$$e^{i\epsilon^2 P_1} = 1 + i\epsilon^2 P_1 + \cdots,$$

which implies

$$[G_1, H] = iP_1 + (\ )1,$$

where $(\ )1$ again indicates a possible multiple of the identity operator. Similarly, we get

$$[G_j, H] = iP_j + (\ )1$$

with possible multiples of the identity operator, for $j = 1, 2, 3$.

A rotation

$$x_j \rightarrow \sum_{k=1}^{3} R_{jk}x_k$$

for $j = 1, 2, 3$ is described by a three-by-three matrix R. We use the matrices

$$R_1(\theta) = \begin{pmatrix} 1 & 0 & 0 \\ 0 & \cos\theta & -\sin\theta \\ 0 & \sin\theta & \cos\theta \end{pmatrix}$$

$$R_2(\theta) = \begin{pmatrix} \cos\theta & 0 & \sin\theta \\ 0 & 1 & 0 \\ -\sin\theta & 0 & \cos\theta \end{pmatrix}$$

$$R_3(\theta) = \begin{pmatrix} \cos\theta & -\sin\theta & 0 \\ \sin\theta & \cos\theta & 0 \\ 0 & 0 & 1 \end{pmatrix}$$

to describe rotations through angles θ about the x, y, and z axis respectively. These matrices are unitary. For each $j = 1, 2, 3$,

$$R_j(\theta + \theta') = R_j(\theta)R_j(\theta')$$

for all real θ and θ', and $R_j(0) = 1$. Stone's theorem tells us that there are Hermitian matrices M_1, M_2, M_3 such that

$$R_j(\theta) = e^{-i\theta M_j}$$

for all real θ. From the power series

$$R_j(\theta) = 1 - i\theta M_j - \cdots$$

to first order in θ, we find

$$M_1 = \begin{pmatrix} 0 & 0 & 0 \\ 0 & 0 & -i \\ 0 & i & 0 \end{pmatrix}$$

$$M_2 = \begin{pmatrix} 0 & 0 & i \\ 0 & 0 & 0 \\ -i & 0 & 0 \end{pmatrix}$$

$$M_3 = \begin{pmatrix} 0 & -i & 0 \\ i & 0 & 0 \\ 0 & 0 & 0 \end{pmatrix}.$$

The commutators of these matrices are

$$M_j M_k - M_k M_j = i\epsilon_{jkm} M_m$$

for $j, k, m = 1, 2, 3$.

To find the commutator of J_1 and J_2 we consider rotations through angles ϵ about the x and y axes and their inverses. To second order in ϵ, the product

$$R_2(-\epsilon)R_1(-\epsilon)R_2(\epsilon)R_1(\epsilon) = 1 + \epsilon^2(M_1 M_2 - M_2 M_1) + \cdots$$
$$= 1 + i\epsilon^2 M_3 + \cdots$$

is the rotation $R_3(-\epsilon^2)$ through the angle $-\epsilon^2$ about the z axis. Therefore to second order in ϵ, the operator

$$e^{i\epsilon J_2}e^{i\epsilon J_1}e^{-i\epsilon J_2}e^{-i\epsilon J_1} = 1 + \epsilon^2[J_1, J_2] + \cdots$$

must be equal up to a phase factor to

$$e^{i\epsilon^2 J_3} = 1 + i\epsilon^2 J_3 + \cdots.$$

It follows that

$$[J_1, J_2] = iJ_3 + (\ )1,$$

with $(\ )1$ again indicating a possible multiple of the identity operator. Similarly, we get

$$[J_j, J_k] = i\epsilon_{jkm}J_m + (\ )1$$

with possible multiples of the identity operator, for $j, k, m = 1, 2, 3$.

For the operator product

$$e^{i\epsilon P_2}e^{i\epsilon J_1}e^{-i\epsilon P_2}e^{-i\epsilon J_1} = 1 + \epsilon^2[J_1, P_2] + \cdots$$

we compute the Galilei-group product

$$(x_1, x_2, x_3) \rightarrow (x_1, x_2\cos\epsilon - x_3\sin\epsilon, x_2\sin\epsilon + x_3\cos\epsilon)$$
$$\rightarrow (x_1, x_2\cos\epsilon - x_3\sin\epsilon + \epsilon, x_2\sin\epsilon + x_3\cos\epsilon)$$
$$\rightarrow (x_1, x_2 + \epsilon\cos\epsilon, x_3 - \epsilon\sin\epsilon)$$
$$\rightarrow (x_1, x_2 + \epsilon\cos\epsilon - \epsilon, x_3 - \epsilon\sin\epsilon).$$

To second order in ϵ, this is the transformation

$$(x_1, x_2, x_3) \rightarrow (x_1, x_2, x_3 - \epsilon^2),$$

which is represented by the operator

$$e^{i\epsilon^2 P_3} = 1 + i\epsilon^2 P_3 + \cdots.$$

Therefore

$$[J_1, P_2] = iP_3 + (\ )1,$$

where $(\ )1$ is another possible multiple of the identity operator. Similarly, we get

$$[J_j, P_k] = i\epsilon_{jkm}P_m + (\ )1$$

and

$$[J_j, G_k] = i\epsilon_{jkm}G_m + (\ )1,$$

with possible multiples of the identity operator, for $j, k, m = 1, 2, 3$.

We have determined the commutators of the generators H, **P**, **J**, **G** up to multiples of the identity operator. Now we eliminate most of the multiples of the identity operator. The commutators are antisymmetric,

$$[A_j, A_k] = -[A_k, A_j],$$

and satisfy the Jacobi identity

$$[[A_j, A_k], A_m] = [[A_m, A_k], A_j] + [[A_j, A_m], A_k].$$

This limits the occurrence of multiples of the identity operator. We can get rid of some of those which do occur by adding them to the generators, because the transformations of state vectors up to phase factors determine the generators only to within addition of real multiples of the identity operator.

For example, by using the Jacobi identity and the commutation relations up to multiples of the identity operator, we get

$$i[P_3, P_1] = [[J_1, P_2], P_1]$$
$$= [[P_1, P_2], J_1] + [[J_1, P_1], P_2] = 0,$$

because multiples of the identity operator are effectively zero inside a commutator. Similarly, we get[10]

$$[P_j, P_k] = 0, \qquad [G_j, G_k] = 0,$$
$$[P_j, H] = 0, \qquad [J_j, H] = 0,$$

for $j, k = 1, 2, 3$.

From the antisymmetry of the commutator it follows that

$$[J_j, J_k] = i\epsilon_{jkm}J_m + i\epsilon_{jkm}b_m,$$

where b_1, b_2, b_3 are real numbers. By adding these multiples of the identity operator to the generators J_1, J_2, J_3, we get

$$[J_j, J_k] = i\epsilon_{jkm}J_m$$

for $j, k, m = 1, 2, 3$.

Using the Jacobi identity again, we get

$$i[J_3, P_3] = [[J_1, J_2], P_3]$$
$$= [[P_3, J_2], J_1] + [[J_1, P_3], J_2]$$
$$= i[J_1, P_1] + i[J_2, P_2]$$

and, similarly,

$$i[J_1, P_1] = i[J_2, P_2] + i[J_3, P_3]$$

from which we see that

$$[J_2, P_2] = 0.$$

---

[10] These operators commute in the sense that the projection operators in their spectral decompositions commute; they can be simultaneously diagonalized. This follows from Stone's theorem and the fact that they generate one-parameter groups of unitary operators which commute. We know that the unitary operators commute up to phase factors. By using power series of the commuting generators on analytic vectors, we eliminate the phase factors, which do not depend on the vectors. Unbounded self-adjoint operators which commute on a dense set of vectors are not always simultaneously diagonalizable. E. Nelson, *loc. cit.*, gives an example of two self-adjoint operators whose spectral projections do not commute, and which do not generate commuting one-parameter groups of unitary operators, even though they are the unique self-adjoint extensions of commuting symmetric operators defined on a common dense domain which is invariant under both operators.

Also, from the Jacobi identity, we get

$$i[J_2, P_3] = [[J_3, J_1], P_3]$$
$$= [[P_3, J_1], J_3] + [[J_3, P_3], J_1]$$
$$= -i[J_3, P_2].$$

Similarly, we get

$$[J_j, P_k] = -[J_k, P_j]$$

for $j, k = 1, 2, 3$. It follows that

$$[J_j, P_k] = i\epsilon_{jkm}P_m + i\epsilon_{jkm}b_m,$$

where b_1, b_2, b_3 are real numbers. By adding these multiples of the identity operator to the generators P_1, P_2, P_3, we get

$$[J_j, P_k] = i\epsilon_{jkm}P_m$$

for $j, k, m = 1, 2, 3$. We can show similarly that by adding real multiples of the identity operator to the generators G_1, G_2, G_3, we get

$$[J_j, G_k] = i\epsilon_{jkm}G_m$$

for $j, k, m = 1, 2, 3$.

From the Jacobi identity again we get

$$i[G_3, H] = [[J_1, G_2], H]$$
$$= [[H, G_2], J_1] + [[J_1, H], G_2]$$
$$= i[J_1, P_2] = -P_3$$

and, similarly,

$$[G_j, H] = iP_j$$

for $j = 1, 2, 3$.

Using the Jacobi identity again, we get

$$i[G_3, P_1] = [[J_1, G_2], P_1]$$
$$= [[P_1, G_2], J_1] + [[J_1, P_1], G_2] = 0$$

and

$$i[G_3, P_3] = [[J_1, G_2], P_3]$$
$$= [[P_3, G_2], J_1] + [[J_1, P_3], G_2]$$
$$= i[G_2, P_2].$$

Similarly, we get

$$[G_j, P_k] = i\delta_{jk}M$$

for $j, k = 1, 2, 3$, where M is a real number.

We have eliminated all multiples of the identity operator except M. This is as far as we can go; we can not get rid of M. The real numbers which could be added to the generators **P**, **J**, **G** were fixed when multiples of the identity operator were eliminated from the commutation relations. Now we cannot add real numbers to these generators without putting multiples of the identity operator back in the commutation relations. But we still can add a real number to the Hamiltonian, because in the commutation relations H occurs only inside commutators. If we considered Lorentz transformations instead of Galilei transformations, then in place of the generators **G** we would have generators **K** which satisfy the commutation relations

$$[K_j, P_k] = i\delta_{jk}\left(\frac{1}{c^2}\right)H$$

for $j, k = 1, 2, 3$. The multiple of the identity operator corresponding to M would be eliminated by adding it to $(1/c^2)H$. Then a real number could not be added to H without putting a multiple of the identity operator back in these commutation relations. For the Galilei group we have the limit

$$\left(\frac{1}{c^2}\right)H \to M$$

as $c \to \infty$. Indeed, for a system of particles we will see that M can be interpreted as the total mass of the system.

In summary we have the commutation relations

$$[G_j, H] = iP_j, \qquad\qquad [J_j, J_k] = i\epsilon_{jkm}J_m,$$

$$[J_j, P_k] = i\epsilon_{jkm}P_m, \qquad [J_j, G_k] = i\epsilon_{jkm}G_m, \qquad [G_j, P_k] = i\delta_{jk}M$$

for $j, k, m = 1, 2, 3$, with M a real number. All the other commutators of $H, \mathbf{P}, \mathbf{J}, \mathbf{G}$ are zero.

By using the commutation relations, we can construct products of the unitary operators of the ten one-parameter subgroups to represent some of the other transformations of the Galilei group. We do a few examples of this in the following applications of the commutation relations.

We can use commutation relations to find operators $e^{iuA}Be^{-iuA}$ either by recognizing the solution of the first-order linear differential equation

$$i\frac{d}{du}e^{iuA}Be^{-iuA} = [e^{iuA}Be^{-iuA}, A]$$

which satisfies the boundary condition that $e^{iuA}Be^{-iuA} = B$ at $u = 0$, or by computing the power-series solution

$$e^{iuA}Be^{-iuA} = B - iu[B, A] - \frac{u^2}{2!}[[B, A], A] - \cdots .$$

Thus the commutation relations imply that $\mathbf{P}$, $\mathbf{J}$, and $\mathbf{G}$ rotate as three-vectors under unitary transformations generated by $\mathbf{J}$. For example,

$$e^{i\alpha J_1} J_3 e^{-i\alpha J_1} = J_3\cos\alpha + J_2\sin\alpha.$$

It follows that

$$e^{i\alpha J_1} e^{-i\theta J_3} e^{-i\alpha J_1} = e^{-i\theta(J_3 \cos\alpha + J_2 \sin\alpha)}.$$

This operator represents a rotation through an angle α about the x axis, followed by a rotation through an angle θ about the z axis, followed by rotation through the angle $-\alpha$ about the x axis. This product is a rotation through the angle θ about an axis in the direction of

$$\boldsymbol{\theta} = (0,\, \theta\sin\alpha,\, \theta\cos\alpha),$$

since rotation through α about the x axis takes the $\boldsymbol{\theta}$ axis to the z axis. We see that the product rotation is represented by the operator $e^{-i\boldsymbol{\theta}\cdot\mathbf{J}}$. For any real three-vector $\boldsymbol{\theta}$ we would find similarly that $e^{-i\boldsymbol{\theta}\cdot\mathbf{J}}$ represents a rotation through an angle $|\boldsymbol{\theta}|$ about an axis in the direction of $\boldsymbol{\theta}$.

Because P_1, P_2, P_3 commute, we have

$$e^{-ir_1 P_1} e^{-ir_2 P_2} e^{-ir_3 P_3} = e^{-i\mathbf{r}\cdot\mathbf{P}}.$$

This operator represents a space translation specified by $\mathbf{r}$. Also, because G_1, G_2, G_3 commute, we have

$$e^{iv_1 G_1} e^{iv_2 G_2} e^{iv_3 G_3} = e^{i\mathbf{v}\cdot\mathbf{G}}.$$

This operator represents a Galilei transformation specified by $\mathbf{v}$.

From the commutation relations it follows that

$$e^{i\mathbf{r}\cdot\mathbf{P}} \mathbf{G} e^{-i\mathbf{r}\cdot\mathbf{P}} = \mathbf{G} + M\mathbf{r}.$$

Therefore

$$e^{i\mathbf{r}\cdot\mathbf{P}} e^{i\mathbf{v}\cdot\mathbf{G}} e^{-i\mathbf{r}\cdot\mathbf{P}} = e^{i\mathbf{v}\cdot(\mathbf{G}+M\mathbf{r})}$$

and

$$e^{-i\mathbf{v}\cdot\mathbf{G}} e^{i\mathbf{r}\cdot\mathbf{P}} e^{i\mathbf{v}\cdot\mathbf{G}} e^{-i\mathbf{r}\cdot\mathbf{P}} = e^{i\mathbf{v}\cdot\mathbf{r}M}.$$

This is a product of four operators which represent a space translation, a Galilei transformation, and their inverses. The product of these four transformations is the identity transformation in the Galilei group, because space translations and Galilei transformations commute. But the operator product is not the identity operator; it is a phase factor. This leads to a superselection rule between different values of the total mass, just as rotation through 2π represented by both 1 and -1 leads to a superselection rule between integral and half-odd-integral angular momenta.[11]

---

[11] See Section 28, *Superselection Rules*.

35. PARTICLE REPRESENTATIONS, INVARIANT INTERACTIONS

Consider a single particle described by operators on the space L^2 of functions $\psi(\mathbf{x})$. For a space translation

$$\mathbf{x} \to \mathbf{x}' = \mathbf{x} + \mathbf{r}$$

we let

$$\psi \to \psi' = e^{-i\mathbf{r}\cdot\mathbf{P}}\psi,$$

where

$$\psi'(\mathbf{x}') = \psi(\mathbf{x}).$$

Thus

$$(e^{-i\mathbf{r}\cdot\mathbf{P}}\psi)(\mathbf{x}) = \psi(\mathbf{x} - \mathbf{r}) = e^{-\mathbf{r}\cdot\nabla}\psi(\mathbf{x})$$

and

$$(\mathbf{P}\psi)(\mathbf{x}) = -i\,\nabla\psi(\mathbf{x}).$$

We work with units in which $\hbar = 1$. Then $\mathbf{P}$ represents the momentum of the particle.

For a rotation $\mathbf{x} \to R\mathbf{x}$ we let

$$(e^{-i\boldsymbol{\theta}\cdot\mathbf{J}}\psi)(\mathbf{x}) = \psi(R^{-1}\mathbf{x}).$$

For example, consider rotations about the x axis. The transformations

$$\psi(x_1, x_2, x_3) \to \psi(x_1, x_2\cos\theta + x_3\sin\theta, -x_2\sin\theta + x_3\cos\theta)$$

define unitary operators which form a one-parameter group as a function of θ, so Stone's theorem tells us that there is a self-adjoint operator J_1 such that

$$(e^{-i\theta J_1}\psi)(x_1, x_2, x_3) = \psi(x_1, x_2\cos\theta + x_3\sin\theta, -x_2\sin\theta + x_3\cos\theta).$$

By comparing the power series

$$\psi(x_1, x_2, x_3) - i\theta(J_1\psi)(x_1, x_2, x_3) - \cdots$$

and

$$\psi(x_1, x_2, x_3) - \theta x_2 \frac{\partial}{\partial x_3}\,\psi(x_1, x_2, x_3) + \theta x_3 \frac{\partial}{\partial x_2}\,\psi(x_1, x_2, x_3) + \cdots$$

to first order in θ, we find

$$(J_1\psi)(x_1, x_2, x_3) = x_2\,\frac{-i\partial}{\partial x_3}\,\psi(x_1, x_2, x_3) - x_3\,\frac{-i\partial}{\partial x_2}\,\psi(x_1, x_2, x_3)$$

or $J_1 = Q_2 P_3 - Q_3 P_2$, where $\mathbf{Q} = (Q_1, Q_2, Q_3)$ are the self-adjoint operators defined by $(\mathbf{Q}\psi)(\mathbf{x}) = \mathbf{x}\,\psi(\mathbf{x})$. Similarly, we get $\mathbf{J} = \mathbf{Q} \times \mathbf{P}$. We are letting $\mathbf{Q}$ represent the position of the particle, so $\mathbf{J}$ represents its angular momentum.

The generators **P** and **J** also are determined by the transformations of the operators **Q** and **P** which represent the position and momentum of the particle. Under space translations

$$\mathbf{Q} \to e^{i\mathbf{r}\cdot\mathbf{P}}\mathbf{Q}e^{-i\mathbf{r}\cdot\mathbf{P}} = \mathbf{Q} + \mathbf{r}$$

and

$$\mathbf{P} \to e^{i\mathbf{r}\cdot\mathbf{P}}\mathbf{P}e^{-i\mathbf{r}\cdot\mathbf{P}} = \mathbf{P}.$$

Under rotations **Q** and **P** rotate as three-vectors. For example,

$$e^{i\theta J_1}Q_3 e^{-i\theta J_1} = Q_2\sin\theta + Q_3\cos\theta.$$

Each transformation determines the commutator of an operator **Q** or **P** and a generator. If we choose generators which differ from these generators **P** and **J** by more than real multiples of the identity operator, then we will get different transformations of **Q** and **P**, because on the space of functions $\psi(\mathbf{x})$ the only operators which commute with **Q** and **P** are multiples of the identity operator.[12] But we cannot add real numbers to **P** or **J** without putting multiples of the identity operator in the commutation relations

$$[J_j, P_k] = i\epsilon_{jkm}P_m$$

and

$$[J_j, J_k] = i\epsilon_{jkm}J_m.$$

Thus the generators **P** and **J** are determined.

For a free particle of mass m the Hamiltonian is

$$H = \frac{1}{2m}\mathbf{P}^2.$$

We work in the Heisenberg picture and let

$$\mathbf{Q}(t) = e^{itH}\mathbf{Q}e^{-itH} = \mathbf{Q} + \frac{t}{m}\mathbf{P}$$

and

$$\mathbf{P}(t) = e^{itH}\mathbf{P}e^{-itH} = \mathbf{P}$$

represent the position and momentum at time t. For Galilei transformations we require that

$$e^{-i\mathbf{v}\cdot\mathbf{G}}\mathbf{Q}(t)e^{i\mathbf{v}\cdot\mathbf{G}} = \mathbf{Q}(t) + \mathbf{v}t$$

and

$$e^{-i\mathbf{v}\cdot\mathbf{G}}\mathbf{P}(t)e^{i\mathbf{v}\cdot\mathbf{G}} = \mathbf{P}(t) + m\mathbf{v}.$$

This means that

$$e^{-i\mathbf{v}\cdot\mathbf{G}}\mathbf{Q}e^{i\mathbf{v}\cdot\mathbf{G}} = \mathbf{Q}$$

[12] See Section 19, *Irreducible Operators, Schur's Lemma.*

and

$$e^{-i\mathbf{v}\cdot\mathbf{G}}\mathbf{P}e^{i\mathbf{v}\cdot\mathbf{G}} = \mathbf{P} + m\mathbf{v}.$$

These transformations are generated by $\mathbf{G} = m\mathbf{Q}$. They determine $\mathbf{G}$ to within addition of real numbers. We cannot add real numbers without putting multiples of the identity operator in the commutation relations

$$[J_j, G_k] = i\epsilon_{jkm}G_m,$$

which are satisfied by $\mathbf{G} = m\mathbf{Q}$. Thus $\mathbf{G}$ is determined.

It is an easy exercise to check that all the commutation relations of the Galilei group are satisfied. We find

$$[G_j, P_k] = i\delta_{jk}m,$$

so $M = m$ is the mass.[13]

From the Galilei-group commutation relations

$$[\mathbf{P}, H] = 0 \quad \text{and} \quad [\mathbf{J}, H] = 0$$

it follows that $\mathbf{P}$ and $\mathbf{J}$ represent quantities which are constants of the motion. This suggests that for a system of more than one particle $\mathbf{P}$ and $\mathbf{J}$ represent the total momentum and total angular momentum. The commutation relation

$$[\mathbf{G}, H] = i\mathbf{P}$$

implies

$$e^{itH}\mathbf{G}e^{-itH} = \mathbf{G} + t\mathbf{P},$$

which suggests that $\mathbf{G}$ represents the center-of-mass position multiplied by the total mass.

Indeed, for a system of two particles we can let

$$H = \frac{1}{2m_1}\mathbf{P}^{(1)2} + \frac{1}{2m_2}\mathbf{P}^{(2)2} + V$$

$$\mathbf{P} = \mathbf{P}^{(1)} + \mathbf{P}^{(2)}$$

$$\mathbf{J} = \mathbf{Q}^{(1)}\times\mathbf{P}^{(1)} + \mathbf{Q}^{(2)}\times\mathbf{P}^{(2)}$$

$$\mathbf{G} = m_1\mathbf{Q}^{(1)} + m_2\mathbf{Q}^{(2)}.$$

---

[13] For a derivation of the description of a particle in terms of the Galilei group, from a more fundamental point of view, see J. M. Jauch, *Foundations of Quantum Mechanics* (Addison-Wesley Publishing Co., Reading, Massachusetts, 1968), Chapters 12 and 13.

The operators representing space translations, rotations, and Galilei transformations are then the same as for two free particles;[14] but time dependence for interacting particles can be obtained by letting V represent the potential energy of interaction. In terms of canonical center-of-mass and relative position and momentum operators

$$\mathbf{Q} = \frac{1}{M}(m_1\mathbf{Q}^{(1)} + m_2\mathbf{Q}^{(2)}), \qquad \mathbf{P} = \mathbf{P}^{(1)} + \mathbf{P}^{(2)},$$

$$\mathbf{q} = \mathbf{Q}^{(1)} - \mathbf{Q}^{(2)}, \qquad\qquad \mathbf{p} = \frac{1}{M}(m_2\mathbf{P}^{(1)} - m_1\mathbf{P}^{(2)}),$$

where $M = m_1 + m_2$, we have

$$\mathbf{J} = \mathbf{Q}\times\mathbf{P} + \mathbf{q}\times\mathbf{p}$$

and

$$\mathbf{G} = M\mathbf{Q}.$$

The Galilei-group commutation relations not involving H are all satisfied. In particular

$$[G_j, P_k] = i\delta_{jk}M,$$

where M is the total mass.

The Galilei-group commutation relations involving H imply that V commutes with $\mathbf{P}$, $\mathbf{J}$ and $\mathbf{Q} = (1/M)\mathbf{G}$. This means that V is a function of $\mathbf{q}$ and $\mathbf{p}$ which is invariant under rotations. For example, because V commutes with $\mathbf{P}$, we have

$$V(\mathbf{Q}, \mathbf{P}, \mathbf{q}, \mathbf{p}) = e^{i\mathbf{r}\cdot\mathbf{P}}\, V(\mathbf{Q}, \mathbf{P}, \mathbf{q}, \mathbf{p})e^{-i\mathbf{r}\cdot\mathbf{P}} = V(\mathbf{Q} + \mathbf{r}, \mathbf{P}, \mathbf{q}, \mathbf{p}),$$

because $\mathbf{P}$ commutes with $\mathbf{P}$, $\mathbf{q}$, and $\mathbf{p}$. Therefore V is independent of $\mathbf{Q}$. Similarly, we see that V is independent of $\mathbf{P}$. Thus V is a function of only $\mathbf{q}$ and $\mathbf{p}$. Because V commutes with $\mathbf{Q}$, $\mathbf{P}$, and $\mathbf{J}$, it is evident that V commutes with $\mathbf{q}\times\mathbf{p}$. It follows that the relative angular momentum $\mathbf{q}\times\mathbf{p}$ is a constant of the motion.

---

[14] This generator $\mathbf{G}$ can be determined from Galilei transformations of the positions and momenta at time zero, but it turns out that the time-dependent positions and momenta also transform as expected. For any $V(\mathbf{q}, \mathbf{p})$ the time-dependent relative position and momentum operators $\mathbf{q}(t) = e^{itH}\mathbf{q}e^{-itH}$ and $\mathbf{p}(t) = e^{itH}\mathbf{p}e^{-itH}$ will be functions of only $\mathbf{q}$ and $\mathbf{p}$. These commute with $\mathbf{G}$, so they are invariant under Galilei transformations, as expected. The time-dependent center-of-mass position and momentum operators $\mathbf{Q}(t) = e^{itH}\mathbf{Q}e^{-itH}$ and $\mathbf{P}(t) = e^{itH}\mathbf{P}e^{-itH}$ will be $\mathbf{Q} + (t/M)\mathbf{P}$ and $\mathbf{P}$ which, with this generator $\mathbf{G}$, transform to $\mathbf{Q}(t) + \mathbf{v}t$ and $\mathbf{P} + M\mathbf{v}$, as expected.

36. PARITY AND TIME REVERSAL

We extend our consideration of space-time transformations to include the *parity* transformation $\mathbf{x} \to -\mathbf{x}$ and the *time-reversal* transformation $t \to -t$. Treating these the same as the transformations of the Galilei group, we get a unitary linear or antiunitary antilinear operator P representing the parity transformation and a unitary linear or antiunitary antilinear operator T representing time reversal.

The parity transformation commutes with rotations and time translations. The parity transformation followed by a space translation,

$$\mathbf{x} \to -\mathbf{x} \to -\mathbf{x} + \mathbf{r},$$

is the same as the inverse space translation followed by the parity transformation,

$$\mathbf{x} \to \mathbf{x} - \mathbf{r} \to -\mathbf{x} + \mathbf{r}.$$

Similarly, the parity transformation followed by a Galilei transformation is the same as the inverse Galilei transformation followed by the parity transformation. Therefore, treating these the same as the transformations of the Galilei group, we get

$$e^{isH}P = (\ )Pe^{isH}, \qquad e^{-i\mathbf{\theta}\cdot\mathbf{J}}P = (\ )Pe^{-i\mathbf{\theta}\cdot\mathbf{J}},$$

$$e^{-i\mathbf{r}\cdot\mathbf{P}}P = (\ )Pe^{i\mathbf{r}\cdot\mathbf{P}} \quad \text{and} \quad e^{i\mathbf{v}\cdot\mathbf{G}}P = (\ )Pe^{-i\mathbf{v}\cdot\mathbf{G}},$$

where $(\ )$ indicates possible phase factors.

Time reversal commutes with space translations and rotations. Time reversal followed by a time translation,

$$t \to -t \to -t + s,$$

is the same as the inverse time translation followed by time reversal,

$$t \to t - s \to -t + s.$$

Time reversal followed by a Galilei transformation,

$$(\mathbf{x}, t) \to (\mathbf{x}, -t) \to (\mathbf{x} + \mathbf{v}(-t), -t) = (\mathbf{x} - \mathbf{v}t, -t),$$

is the same as the inverse Galilei transformation followed by time reversal,

$$(\mathbf{x}, t) \to (\mathbf{x} - \mathbf{v}t, t) \to (\mathbf{x} - \mathbf{v}t, -t).$$

Therefore, treating these the same as the transformations of the Galilei group, we get

$$e^{-i\mathbf{r}\cdot\mathbf{P}}T = (\quad)Te^{-i\mathbf{r}\cdot\mathbf{P}}, \qquad e^{-i\boldsymbol{\theta}\cdot\mathbf{J}}T = (\quad)Te^{-i\boldsymbol{\theta}\cdot\mathbf{J}},$$

$$e^{isH}T = (\quad)Te^{-isH}, \qquad e^{i\mathbf{v}\cdot\mathbf{G}}T = (\quad)Te^{-i\mathbf{v}\cdot\mathbf{G}},$$

where again ( ) indicates possible phase factors.

We assume that the spectrum of the Hamiltonian has a lower bound but no upper bound. Then the linear-antilinear question for P and T is settled by the following.

Theorem 36.1.   If the negative part of the spectrum of H is bounded and the positive part is unbounded, then P is linear and T is antilinear.

Proof.   Suppose P is antilinear and antiunitary. Then P has an inverse P^{-1} which is antilinear and antiunitary. The operator $P^{-1}HP$ is self-adjoint: $\chi = (P^{-1}HP)^{\dagger}\psi$ means that $(\phi, \chi) = (P^{-1}HP\phi, \psi)$ for every vector ϕ in the domain of $P^{-1}HP$, or that $(P\phi, P\chi) = (HP\phi, P\psi)$ for every vector $P\phi$ in the domain of H, or that $P\chi = H^{\dagger}P\psi$, which is the same as $P\chi = HP\psi$, or $\chi = P^{-1}HP\psi$. Let E_x denote the projection operators in the spectral decomposition of H. The projection operators in the spectral decomposition of $P^{-1}HP$ are $P^{-1}E_xP$: it is easy to check that the set of operators $P^{-1}E_xP$ is a spectral family of projection operators; for any vector ϕ, and any vector ψ in the domain of $P^{-1}HP$,

$$(\phi, P^{-1}HP\psi) = (P\phi, HP\psi)^* = \int_{-\infty}^{\infty} x \, d(P\phi, E_xP\psi)^* = \int_{-\infty}^{\infty} x \, d(\phi, P^{-1}E_xP\psi).$$

Therefore the spectrum of $P^{-1}HP$ is the same as the spectrum of H. For any vectors ψ and ϕ and real number s

$$(\phi, e^{-isP^{-1}HP}\psi) = \int_{-\infty}^{\infty} e^{-isx} \, d(\phi, P^{-1}E_xP\psi) = \int_{-\infty}^{\infty} e^{-isx} \, d(P\phi, E_xP\psi)^*$$

$$= (P\phi, e^{isH}P\psi)^* = (\phi, P^{-1}e^{isH}P\psi),$$

so

$$e^{-isP^{-1}HP} = P^{-1}e^{isH}P.$$

From

$$e^{isH}P = \omega(s)Pe^{isH},$$

with $\omega(s)$ a phase factor, we get

$$e^{-isP^{-1}HP} = P^{-1}\omega(s)Pe^{isH} = \omega(s)^* e^{isH},$$

which implies that

$$P^{-1}HP = -H + b.$$

with b a real number. Therefore the spectrum of $-H + b$ is the same as the spectrum of H. This contradicts the assumptions about the spectrum of H.

Similarly, if T is linear and unitary, then from

$$e^{isH}T = \omega(s)Te^{-isH},$$

with $\omega(s)$ a phase factor, we get

$$T^{-1}HT = -H + b$$

with b a real number, which implies that H and $-H + b$ have the same spectrum. If P is linear and T is antilinear, then we do not get these contradictions. This proves the theorem.

The product of two parity transformations is the identity transformation of space-time coordinates, as is the product of two time-reversal transformations. Therefore we assume that P^2 and T^2 are phase-factor multiples of the identity operator. From $TT^2 = T^2T$ it follows that T^2 is real, so $T^2 = \pm1$.

We have

$$e^{isH}P = \omega(s)Pe^{isH}$$

with a phase factor $\omega(s)$. Multiplying on both left and right by P, we get

$$Pe^{isH}P^2 = \omega(s)P^2e^{isH}P.$$

Cancelling the phase factor P^2, we get

$$Pe^{isH} = \omega(s)e^{isH}P = \omega(s)^2Pe^{isH}.$$

Therefore $\omega(s) = \pm1$. But $\omega(s_1 + s_2) = \omega(s_1)\omega(s_2)$, because

$$\omega(s_1 + s_2)Pe^{i(s_1+s_2)H} = e^{i(s_1+s_2)H}P = e^{is_1H}\omega(s_2)Pe^{is_2H}$$
$$= \omega(s_1)\omega(s_2)Pe^{is_1H}e^{is_2H}.$$

Therefore $\omega(s) = \omega(s/2)\omega(s/2) = 1$. Thus we get

$$e^{isH}P = Pe^{isH}$$

and $HP = PH$. Eliminating the phase factors similarly, we get

$$e^{-i\theta\cdot J}P = Pe^{-i\theta\cdot J}$$

and $JP = PJ$.

We have

$$e^{isH}T = \omega(s)Te^{-isH}$$

with a phase factor $\omega(s)$. Multiplying on both left and right by T, we get

$$Te^{isH}T^2 = T\omega(s)Te^{-isH}T = \omega(s)^*T^2e^{-isH}T.$$

Cancelling T^2, we get

$$Te^{isH} = \omega(s)^*e^{-isH}T.$$

Multiplying on the left by e^{isH} and on the right by e^{-isH}, we get

$$e^{isH}T = \omega(s)^* T e^{-isH}.$$

Therefore $\omega(s) = \omega(s)^*$ so $\omega(s) = \pm 1$. As in the preceding paragraph, we get $\omega(s_1 + s_2) = \omega(s_1)\omega(s_2)$, which implies that $\omega(s) = 1$. Thus we get

$$e^{isH}T = T e^{-isH}.$$

Because T is antilinear, it follows that

$$iHT = T(-i)H = iTH$$

or $HT = TH$. Eliminating the phase factors similarly, we get

$$e^{i\mathbf{v}\cdot\mathbf{G}}T = T e^{-i\mathbf{v}\cdot\mathbf{G}}$$

and $\mathbf{G}T = T\mathbf{G}$.

Allowing for phase factors, we have

$$\mathbf{P}P = -P\mathbf{P} + \mathbf{b}P$$

with real numbers $\mathbf{b} = (b_1, b_2, b_3)$. Using the commutation relations of $\mathbf{P}$ and $\mathbf{J}$, we get

$$ib_3 = iP_3P + iPP_3 = (J_1P_2 - P_2J_1)P + P(J_1P_2 - P_2J_1)$$
$$= J_1b_2P - b_2PJ_1 = 0.$$

Thus we get $\mathbf{P}P = -P\mathbf{P}$. Similarly, using the commutation relations of $\mathbf{G}$ with $\mathbf{J}$, we get $\mathbf{G}P = -P\mathbf{G}$.

Allowing for phase factors, we have

$$\mathbf{J}T = -T\mathbf{J} + \mathbf{b}T$$

with real numbers $\mathbf{b} = (b_1, b_2, b_3)$. Using the commutation relations of $\mathbf{J}$ and the antilinearity of T, we get

$$ib_3T = iJ_3T + iTJ_3 = iJ_3T - TiJ_3$$
$$= (J_1J_2 - J_2J_1)T - T(J_1J_2 - J_2J_1)$$
$$= J_1b_2T - J_2b_1T - b_1TJ_2 + b_2TJ_1 = 0.$$

Thus we get $\mathbf{J}T = -T\mathbf{J}$. Similarly, using the commutation relations of $\mathbf{P}$ with $\mathbf{J}$, we get $\mathbf{P}T = -T\mathbf{P}$.

The properties of P and T are easily summarized: P is a unitary linear operator which commutes with H and $\mathbf{J}$ and anticommutes with $\mathbf{P}$ and $\mathbf{G}$; T is an antiunitary antilinear operator which commutes with H and $\mathbf{G}$ and anticommutes with $\mathbf{P}$ and $\mathbf{J}$.

Consider a single free particle of mass m. We have $\mathbf{P}P = -P\mathbf{P}$ and $\mathbf{Q}P = -P\mathbf{Q}$, because $\mathbf{G} = m\mathbf{Q}$. From this it follows that P does commute with $H = (1/2m)\mathbf{P}^2$ and $\mathbf{J} = \mathbf{Q} \times \mathbf{P}$ as required. We have the correct parity transformations

$$P^\dagger \mathbf{Q} P = -\mathbf{Q}$$

and

$$P^\dagger \mathbf{P} P = -\mathbf{P}$$

for the position and momentum. These determine P up to a phase factor on the space of functions $\psi(\mathbf{x})$: if P and P' are unitary operators which anticommute with $\mathbf{Q}$ and $\mathbf{P}$, then $P'P^\dagger$ is a unitary operator which commutes with $\mathbf{Q}$ and $\mathbf{P}$, so $P'P^\dagger$ is a phase-factor multiple of the identity operator, and $P' = P'P^\dagger P$ differs from P only by a phase factor. Therefore, up to a phase factor, P must be defined by $(P\psi)(\mathbf{x}) = \psi(-\mathbf{x})$ as expected, because this operator P is unitary and does anticommute with $\mathbf{Q}$ and $\mathbf{P}$.

Similarly, for a single free particle of mass m, we have $\mathbf{P}T = -T\mathbf{P}$ and $\mathbf{Q}T = T\mathbf{Q}$, because $\mathbf{G} = m\mathbf{Q}$. From this it follows that T does commute with H and anticommute with $\mathbf{J}$ as required. For a Hermitian operator A transformations $\psi \to T\psi$ of state vectors produce transformations

$$(\psi, A\psi) \to (T\psi, AT\psi) = (T\psi, AT\psi)^* = (\psi, T^{-1}AT\psi)$$

of expectation values, which are equivalent to the transformation

$$A \to T^{-1}AT$$

of the operator. We have the correct time-reversal transformations

$$T^{-1}\mathbf{Q}T = \mathbf{Q}$$

and

$$T^{-1}\mathbf{P}T = -\mathbf{P}$$

for the position and momentum. These determine T up to a phase factor on the space of functions $\psi(\mathbf{x})$: if T and T' are antiunitary operators which commute with $\mathbf{Q}$ and anticommute with $\mathbf{P}$, then $T'T^{-1}$ is a unitary operator which commutes with $\mathbf{Q}$ and $\mathbf{P}$, so $T'T^{-1}$ is a phase-factor multiple of the identity operator, and $T' = T'T^{-1}T$ differs from T only by a phase factor. Therefore, up to a phase factor, T must be defined by $(T\psi)(\mathbf{x}) = \psi(\mathbf{x})^*$, because this operator T is antilinear and antiunitary and does commute with $\mathbf{Q}$ and anticommute with $\mathbf{P}$.

See *Exercise and Application* 2.

EXERCISES AND
APPLICATIONS

Numbers in [ ] refer to relevant sections of the text.

1. [5, 6, 11] Let A and B be bounded operators on a complex separable Hilbert space. Show that if $(\psi, A\psi) = (\psi, B\psi)$ for every vector ψ of length one, then $A = B$. Suppose A and B are unbounded operators with the same dense domain. Show that if $(\psi, A\psi) = (\psi, B\psi)$ for every vector ψ of length one in their domain, then $A = B$.

2. [14, 15, 33] Consider the operator $e^{i2\pi J_3}$ which represents a rotation through an angle -2π about the z axis. A state should not be changed by this transformation. Assume there is a real number b such that $e^{i2\pi J_3} = e^{i2\pi b}$. Let E_x be the projection operators in the spectral decomposition of J_3. Show that for any vector ψ

$$\int_{-\infty}^{\infty} |e^{i2\pi x} - e^{i2\pi b}|^2 d\|E_x\psi\|^2 = 0$$

and that consequently the spectrum of J_3 consists of points $b + m$ for integers m. In particular J_3 has no continuous spectrum.

3. [11–14, 18] Consider the space L^2 of functions $\psi(x)$ for $0 \leq x \leq 2\pi$. Letting $(L_3\psi)(x) = -i(d/dx)\psi(x)$ does not completely define a Hermitian operator L_3. This operator will be unbounded. Its domain has to be specified. Show that to get a Hermitian operator, one must choose a real number b and let the domain consist of vectors ψ such that $\psi(2\pi) = e^{i2\pi b}\psi(0)$. For each different $e^{i2\pi b}$ one gets a different Hermitian operator L_3; see Riesz and Nagy, Section 119. For its eigenvectors, which must

130

be in the domain, one gets functions $e^{i(b+m)x}$ for integers m. Its spectrum consists of the points $b + m$ for integers m. Now consider the operator $L_3 = Q_1 P_2 - Q_2 P_1$ on the space of square-integrable functions $\psi(\mathbf{x})$. Show that $\psi(\mathbf{x}) = e^{-\mathbf{x}^2}$ is a vector which is in the domain of L_3 and that $L_3 \psi = 0$ for this vector. Therefore it is correct to choose $b = 0$ when L_3 is expressed in terms of the spherical coordinate $x = \tan^{-1}(x_2/x_1)$. It follows that the spectrum of L_3 consists of integers.

4. [11–18] Let $V(r)$ be a real function. Suppose there are positive numbers a and c such that

$$\int_0^a V(r)^2 r^2 \, dr < c^2$$

and $|V(r)| < c$ for $r > a$. In particular $V(r)$ cannot be more singular than $r^{-3/2}$ at $r = 0$. Then there is a self-adjoint operator

$$H = \mathbf{P}^2 + V([\mathbf{Q}^2]^{1/2}).$$

Its domain is the domain of $\mathbf{P}^2$. (See T. Kato, *Trans. Amer. Math. Soc.* **70**, 195 (1951).) Consider a spherically symmetric vector $\psi(\mathbf{x}) = f(r)$ with $r = (\mathbf{x}^2)^{1/2}$. Suppose $f(r) \sim r^b$ as $r \to 0$. Show that if b is negative or if $0 < b < \frac{1}{2}$, then ψ is not in the domain of H so, in particular, ψ is not an eigenvector of H. For all except $b = -1$ it is easy to see that ψ is not in the domain of $\mathbf{P}^2$ by considering

$$\int |\nabla^2 \psi|^2 \, d\mathbf{x} \sim \int_0^c \left| r^{-2} \frac{d}{dr} r^2 \frac{d}{dr} f(r) \right|^2 r^2 \, dr.$$

For $b < -\frac{1}{2}$ one can show that ψ is not in the domain of P_3 and therefore not in the domain of $\mathbf{P}^2$ by considering

$$\int \left| \frac{d}{dx_3} \psi \right|^2 d\mathbf{x} \sim \int_0^c \left| \frac{d}{dr} f(r) \right|^2 r^2 \, dr.$$

5. [18, 25] Let F be the unitary operator defined by the Fourier transform, and let $\mathbf{L} = \mathbf{Q} \times \mathbf{P}$. Show that $FQ = -PF$ and that $FL = LF$. Suppose ψ is an eigenvector of $\mathbf{L}^2$ and L_3. Show that $F\psi$ is an eigenvector of $\mathbf{L}^2$ and L_3 with the same eigenvalues. It follows that the dependence of $(F\psi)(\mathbf{k})$ on the angles of $\mathbf{k}$ is the same as the dependence of $\psi(\mathbf{x})$ on the angles of $\mathbf{x}$. In particular, for a state represented by an eigenvector of $\mathbf{L}^2$ and L_3, the probability distribution for the direction of the momentum is the same as the probability distribution for the direction of the position.

6. [19] The eigenvectors of the Hamiltonian for a three-dimensional harmonic oscillator span a space of square-integrable functions $\psi(\mathbf{x})$ which is invariant under the operators $\mathbf{Q}$ and $\mathbf{P}$. Show how it follows that this is the entire space of square-integrable functions $\psi(\mathbf{x})$.

7. [17, 25, 26, 28] Consider a system which has superselection rules with the discrete structure described by projection operators I_k. Suppose that for a given state there is no uncertainty for each of a complete set of commuting Hermitian operators which represent measurable quantities. Show that there is only one density matrix which represents this state and that it is a projection $|\psi\rangle\langle\psi|$ for a vector ψ which is in a subspace onto which an I_k projects.

8. [13, 15, 16] Consider operators on an n-dimensional space. Let A be a Hermitian operator which has m different eigenvalues. Then $m \leq n$. Suppose B is an operator which is a function of A. Show that there is a polynomial

$$f(x) = c_0 + c_1 x + c_2 x^2 + \cdots + c_{m-1} x^{m-1}$$

such that $B = f(A)$. Suppose B is a function of commuting Hermitian operators $A_1, A_2, \ldots, A_N$. Show that B is a polynomial in which the highest power of each operator $A_1, A_2, \ldots, A_N$ is less than the number of its different eigenvalues.

9. [20] For a finite-dimensional space weak limits are not needed to get the von Neumann algebra generated by a set of noncommuting Hermitian operators. Every operator in the von Neumann algebra is a polynomial of the given Hermitian operators. Prove this as follows. Let each operator B on the n-dimensional space have matrix elements b_{jk} for $j, k = 1, 2, \ldots, n$, with respect to some orthonormal basis. Consider the n^2-dimensional linear space of these $n \times n$ matrices. An inner product is defined by

$$(A, B) = \mathrm{Tr}\,(A^\dagger B) = \sum_{j,k=1}^{n} a_{jk}^* b_{jk}$$

for all $n \times n$ matrices A and B. Let Ω be an operator on this n^2-dimensional space. It has matrix elements $\omega_{jk,rs}$ such that for any $n \times n$ matrix B the matrix elements of ΩB are $\sum_{r,s=1}^{n} \omega_{jk,rs} b_{rs}$ for $j, k = 1, 2, \ldots, n$. In particular for each $n \times n$ matrix B there is an $n^2 \times n^2$ matrix $\Omega(B)$ such that $\Omega(B)A = BA$ for every $n \times n$ matrix A, or $\omega(B)_{jk,rs} = \delta_{ks} b_{jr}$. Show that $\Omega(B^\dagger) = \Omega(B)^\dagger$. Consider the set of all polynomials of the given $n \times n$ Hermitian matrices. This is a subspace of the n^2-dimensional space of all $n \times n$ matrices. Let Λ be the projection operator onto this subspace, and let $\lambda_{jk,rs}$ be its matrix elements. For each $k, s = 1, 2, \ldots, n$ let E^{ks} be the $n \times n$ matrix whose elements are $e^{ks}{}_{jr} = \lambda_{jk,rs}$ for $j, r = 1, 2, \ldots, n$. Since the $n \times n$ identity matrix is a polynomial of any $n \times n$ Hermitian matrix, it is in this subspace. Show that therefore $\sum_{s=1}^{n} e^{ks}{}_{js} = \delta_{jk}$. If A and B are polynomials of the given $n \times n$ Hermitian matrices, then $\Omega(B)A = BA$ and $\Omega(B)^\dagger A = B^\dagger A$ are polynomials, so $\Omega(B)\Lambda = \Lambda\Omega(B)\Lambda$ and $\Omega(B)^\dagger\Lambda = \Lambda\Omega(B)^\dagger\Lambda$, which implies that $\Omega(B)\Lambda = \Lambda\Omega(B)$. Show that therefore $BE^{ks} = E^{ks}B$ for all polynomials B and all ks. Let C be an $n \times n$ matrix which commutes with every $n \times n$ matrix which commutes with the given $n \times n$ Hermitian matrices. Then C commutes with each E^{ks}. Show that $\Lambda C = C$, which means that C is a polynomial of the given $n \times n$ Hermitian matrices. Thus if an operator is in the von Neumann algebra, it is a polynomial.

BIBLIOGRAPHY

Bargmann, V., *Ann. Math.* **59**, 1 (1954).

Bargmann, V., *J. Math. Phys.* **5**, 862 (1964).

Birkhoff, G., and S. MacLane, *A Survey of Modern Algebra* (The Macmillan Co., New York, 1965).

Dell'Antonio, G. F., *Commun. Math. Phys.* **2**, 384 (1966).

Dixmier, J., *Les algebres d'operateurs dans l'espace Hilbertien* (Gauthiers-Villars, Paris, 1957).

Dirac, P. A. M., *The Principles of Quantum Mechanics*, Fourth Edition (Oxford University Press, 1958).

Dunford, N., and J. T. Schwartz, *Linear Operators*, Part II (Interscience Publishers, New York, 1963).

Emch, G., *J. Math. Phys.* **7**, 1413 (1966).

Feller, W., *An Introduction to Probability Theory and Its Applications*, Volume II (John Wiley and Sons, New York, 1966).

Gleason, A. M., *J. Math. Mech.* **6**, 885 (1957).

Hardy, G. H., and W. W. Rogosinski, *Fourier Series* (Cambridge University Press, 1950).

Jauch, J. M., *Foundations of Quantum Mechanics* (Addison-Wesley Publishing Co., Reading, Massachusetts, 1968).

Jauch, J. M., *Helv. Phys. Acta* **33**, 711 (1960).

Jauch, J. M., and B. Misra, *Helv. Phys. Acta* **38**, 30 (1965).

Kadison, R. V., and J. R. Ringrose, *Commun. Math. Phys.* **4**, 32 (1967).

Langerholc, J., *J. Math. Phys.* **6**, 1210 (1965).

Marchand, J. P., *Distributions* (North-Holland Publishing Co., Amsterdam; Interscience Publishers, New York; 1962).

Merzbacher, E., *Quantum Mechanics* (John Wiley and Sons, New York, 1961).

Messiah, A., *Quantum Mechanics*, Vol. I (North-Holland Publishing Co., Amsterdam; Interscience Publishers, New York; 1962).

Naimark, M. A., *Normed Rings*, translated by L. F. Boron (P. Noordhoff, Groningen, 1960).

Nelson, E., *Ann. Math.* **70**, 572 (1959).

Pontrjagin, L., *Topological Groups*, Second Edition, translated by A. Brown (Gordon and Breach, New York, 1966).

Riesz, F., and B. Sz.-Nagy, *Functional Analysis*, translated by L. F. Boron (F. Ungar Publishing Co., New York, 1955).

Stone, M. H., *Linear Transformations in Hilbert Space* (American Mathematical Society, New York, 1932).

Taylor, A. E., *Functional Analysis* (John Wiley and Sons, New York, 1958).

Voisin, J., *J. Math. Phys.* **6**, 1519 (1965).

von Neumann, J., *Mathematical Foundations of Quantum Mechanics* (Princeton University Press, Princeton, New Jersey, 1955).

Wigner, E. P., *Ann. Math.* **40**, 149 (1939).

Wigner, E. P., *Group Theory* (Academic Press, New York, 1959).

INDEX